An exhibition of

BRITISH
MILITARY VEHICLES

(by kind permission of the Secretary of State for Defence)

at the

FIGHTING VEHICLES
RESEARCH & DEVELOPMENT
ESTABLISHMENT

Chertsey . . . 1966

arranged by

The Fighting Vehicles Research & Development Establishment

in collaboration with

The Society of Motor Manufacturers
and Traders

A Message from

THE SECRETARY OF STATE FOR DEFENCE

I AM pleased to have this opportunity of welcoming visitors to the 1966 exhibition of British military vehicles. Modern Armies march on wheels. They need vehicles of all kinds, and in their thousands; but all alike must be versatile, reliable and tough. We are fortunate to be able to draw on the skill and experience of the British Motor Industry to meet our worldwide needs; and over the years we have developed a firm and fruitful relationship with member companies of the Society of Motor Manufacturers and Traders.

What you see here bears witness to that relationship, and the benefit that it has brought to our national Defence.

Denis Healey

THE RIGHT HON. DENIS HEALEY, M.B.E., M.P.

Secretary of State for Defence

A Message from

D1633670

THE PRESIDENT ᴏꜰ ᴛʜᴇ

CLOSE collaboration between the Fighting Vehicles Research and Development Establishment and the British motor industry has resulted in the design and production of the many and various military vehicles and trailers illustrated and described in this catalogue. Many of these sturdy vehicles are also suitable for civil purposes.

The display for which this publication has been primarily produced is a unique and intensely interesting event and one to which I want to give a special welcome to many visitors from all parts of the world.

The special purposes for which many of the vehicles are intended posed complex problems both in design and manufacture, and the success with which such difficulties were met and overcome will be evident from the way in which they are put through their paces at the display.

The Society of Motor Manufacturers and Traders has received the greatest co-operation from the F.V.R.D.E. in the organisation of a display which surpasses all its predecessors in diversity and imaginative presentation.

Sɪʀ Pᴀᴛʀɪᴄᴋ Hᴇɴɴᴇssʏ
President of the Society of Motor Manufacturers and Traders

ABOUT THE EXHIBITION

With the accent on mobility, numerous spectacular demonstrations will be presented throughout the Exhibition to show the versatility and effectiveness of British military vehicles. For many of them the description 'military' is even then too limiting in its scope, for they are readily adaptable to civilian use.

Included in the programme will be a grand procession in which vehicles ranging from motor cycle to tank transporter will be driven over the suspension course.

Static exhibitions of about 150 wheeled and tracked vehicles, of equipment and—in the Research and Test Laboratory—functional testing of components will be accompanied by vehicles under test on full load and in arctic and tropical temperatures.

The test tracks on which the demonstrations take place and the Workshops and Laboratory are fully described on pages vi to xii.

THE FIGHTING VEHICLES RESEARCH AND DEVELOPMENT ESTABLISHMENT

Aerial View of the Main Establishment.

F.V.R.D.E. is responsible for the research, design and development of tracked and wheeled vehicles to meet the requirements of the Services and certain other Government Departments.

The interpretation of the performance characteristics and the general design and layout of new equipments and components are done at F.V.R.D.E., but the greater part of the detail design and the construction of prototypes is undertaken by Industrial Firms under development contracts. Many of these firms are members of the S.M.M.T. Certain specialist equipments for which there are no civilian counterparts are designed entirely at F.V.R.D.E.

Development trials are carried out by the Establishment to prove designs both from the technical and user aspects, after which equipments are offered to the Service Departments for formal acceptance. F.V.R.D.E. continues to be actively interested in an equipment throughout its service life, producing any designs for modification or improvement which may be called for by the Services.

In order to carry out these functions, F.V.R.D.E. is equipped with Workshops and testing facilities which are complementary to the Research and Design Divisions.

The Workshops

Though the normal function of the very fully equipped workshops is to maintain and modify vehicles undergoing trials, it is not infrequently called upon to produce pilot models of new designs for components and assemblies and has on many occasions built complete vehicles.

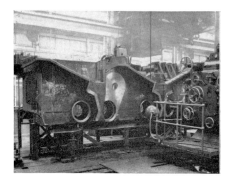

Heavy Machine Shop, Machining a Prototype Tracked Vehicle Hull.

The woodworking shop is much larger than might be expected as it is responsible for the construction of the full scale wooden 'mock-ups' that are a vital phase in the development cycle of a fighting vehicle.

The Workshops has its own engine test cell equipped with two dynamometers. One has a capacity of 350 h.p., the other of 1,000 h.p. capacity has a tilting bed.

Many defects that occur during trials require detailed analysis of the cause of failure before modifications can be designed and fitted. The Workshops has a Technical Section to carry out these investigations and reports its findings to the Design Staff.

Testing Facilities

The testing facilities for vehicles and components in or close to the Establishment fall into three categories. Firstly there are the laboratory and static types of test equipment largely used for complete vehicle, sub-assembly, and component development work which are provided by the Engineering Test Laboratory. Secondly there are the vehicle calibration and basic performance test facilities, which are artificial in nature, situated in the area of the Main Test Track and finally there are the natural courses at Bagshot and Long Valley which allow vehicles to be tested for reliability and durability under selected severe Service conditions.

In addition, F.V.R.D.E. has its own ranges at Kirkcudbright where trials of vehicle weapon systems are carried out. There is also a test site on Horsea Island, Portsmouth, where the more advanced trials with amphibious vehicles are made prior to their final tests across natural water obstacles.

The Research Test Laboratory

This Laboratory carries out development testing for the Design and Research Divisions.

Some of the facilities are designed to accommodate and test complete vehicles whereas others handle sub-assemblies or components.

The Vehicle Dynamometer can accommodate the largest vehicle. The tractive output from each side of the vehicle is absorbed by two dynamometer brakes, which enables an analysis to be made of the installed power and transmission system.

The Drum Dynamometer can make an analysis of the installed power and transmission systems of the smaller vehicles with output powers up to 150 h.p. Tropical temperatures with solar radiation can be simulated whilst vehicles are on the dynamometer.

Fan and Aircleaner Laboratories are equipped to carry out development on vehicle cooling fans and also to develop and test engine aircleaners which must have the highest efficiency if they are to be effective on Service vehicles. The Tyre Test

Laboratory is equipped with three tyre testing machines capable of imposing loads of 1 to 10 tons.

There are three fully instrumented engine test cells, giving an engine test facility with a capability range of up to 1,000 h.p.

Eight Cylinder Diesel Engine on 1000 H.P. Test Bed.

A number of other specialised test equipments or rigs are permanently installed in the Laboratory, but in addition a comprehensive stock of test apparatus is available which can be built into rigs on an ad hoc basis.

The Engineering Test Laboratory is also equipped with tropical and low temperature chambers which are large enough to accommodate complete vehicles. The Tropical chamber can produce an environmental temperature of 200°F, with adjustable simulated solar radiation up to tropical intensity. The humidity can be maintained at any desired level in any temperature up to 125°F.

The Low Temperature Chamber can work down to minus 60°F. At minus 40°F it can remove heat at the rate of 600,000 B.Th.U. per hour which enables cold starting tests to be made on the largest of vehicle engines.

The Main Test Track

There is a two mile perimeter circuit of high grade asphalt road 35 feet wide, roughly eliptical in plan, laid on a cement stabilised subgrade strong enough to permit continuous running by the heaviest tracked or wheeled vehicles. There is a straight and level section $\frac{1}{4}$ mile long but the remainder of the circuit generally follows the undulations of the site. There is an inner loop across the south east curve of the perimeter circuit built to the same strength specification. This loop was laid out to make the most effective use of a small hill feature in order to provide a series of sharp curves and short but steep gradients.

Situated within the main perimeter are a number of specially designed test facilities which are used to calibrate vehicle performance. A number of these can also be used for accelerated reliability trials on certain design aspects of a vehicle. These facilities permit close control of test, under accurately repeatable conditions.

Aerial View of part of the Main Test Track Area.

The more important of these facilities are the Suspension Test Courses, the Test Slopes, the Wading Pit, and the Tilting Platform. There are also a number of gauges for determining belly clearance, suspension articulation limits, landing-craft and aircraft loading clearances and similar parameters of vehicle design.

The Winch Test House, together with its supplementary equipment provides a means of assessing a number of other aspects of vehicle design apart from its primary purpose of winch and winch-gear testing.

The Bagshot and Long Valley Courses

These two sites provide natural courses which simulate certain severe Service conditions. They are primarily used to assess reliability and robustness but they are also valuable for comparative assessment of vehicles operating under these conditions and for obtaining crew reaction.

Bagshot Heath

The three Bagshot Heath courses are laid out over a severely eroded area of sandy gravel.

The Rough Road course is a two mile pot-holed circuit of water bound macadam construction which is used by all wheeled vehicles.

Part of the Alpine Course, Bagshot Heath.

The Alpine Course provides a three and a half mile circuit of natural surface track containing many steep gradients. It is used by both light wheeled vehicles and light tracked vehicles.

The Red Road course is a flat cross country track about two and a quarter miles long. Its surface is also natural and it is used by all classes of wheeled vehicles as well as by light tracked vehicles.

Long Valley

Two courses, one about four miles long and the other about two and a half miles long, over a generally flat area of sand and sandy

Towing Trials of A.V.R.E. Trailer — Long Valley.

gravel, are used respectively for wheeled and tracked vehicles. These courses are quite natural and have no maintenance work done on them. Their surface condition is very dependent on the weather and the effects of any previous traffic.

In wet weather they provide very rough muddy cross-country going, in dry weather they are extremely dusty. The soil in this area is particularly abrasive and rapidly reveals any lack of protection of exposed suspension, steering or drive components.

CATALOGUE

OF

VEHICLES

IN THE

STATIC

EXHIBITION

PART 1 — Pages 1 to 220

This section of the catalogue shows vehicles for military use, produced by the British Motor Industry and sponsored by, or developed in co-operation with, F. V. R. D. E.

PART 2 — Pages 222 to 229

This section of the catalogue shows exhibits for military use sponsored and produced by British industry but not in co-operation with F. V. R. D. E.

Motor Cycle (B.S.A. B40 W.D.)

(Project State—Undergoing User Trials)

Description: This motor cycle is based on the commercial component of the B.S.A. B40 model but incorporates features to improve the suitability for use in a military environment. These features include a special engine air filtration system with a dust proof carburettor and improved protection for the rear chain and front forks. To ensure long life the engine is down rated and a compression ratio of 7 : 1 has been chosen to suit military fuels.

F.V. Specification Number: Chassis 9328.

Height: 3′ 7″ (*1·1 m.*).   Length: 6′ 9″ (*2·06 m.*).
Width: 2′ 5½″ (*0·75 m.*).   Wheelbase: 4′ 5½″ (*1·35 m.*).
Weight: Unladen 358 lb. (*161 kg.*).

PERFORMANCE DATA

Speed, average maximum:
    Road 55 m.p.h. (*88·6 km./h.*).
    C.C. 25 m.p.h. (*40·3 km./h.*).
Range of action at average maximum speed: 250 miles (*403 km.*).
Maximum climbing ability: 1 in 2.

TECHNICAL DATA

Power Unit
Type: B.S.A. Single cylinder o.h.v.
Displacement: 343 c.c. (20·9 cu. in.).
Gross B.H.P.: 18 at 6,000 r.p.m.
Nett torque (lb. ft.): 17 at 4,000 r.p.m.
Ignition type: 6 volt coil.

Fuel System
Type: Gravity feed.
Type of fuel: Gasoline.
Air cleaner: Dry—paper element.
Fuel capacity: 3½ gallons (*15·9 litres*).

Engine Lubrication
System: Dry sump—gear type oil pump.

Engine Cooling
System: Air cooled.

Wheels
Front: Rims WM1-20.
Rear: Rims WM3-18.
Front: Tyres 3·00″ × 20″ (trials universal).
Rear: Tyres 3·50″ × 18″ (trials universal).
Tyre pump: Hand.

Transmission
Clutch: Multi-plate.
Gearbox: 4 speed.
Ratios: Top 6·53 : 1. Bottom 20·1 : 1.
Final drive: Chain drive.

Brakes
Foot: Mechanical to rear wheel.
Hand: Mechanical to front wheel.

Steering
System: Handlebar.
Turning circle: R.H. 13′ 9″ (*4·19 m.*). L.H. 13′ 6″ (*4·12 m.*).

Suspension
Front: Telescopic—coil spring hydraulically damped.
Rear: Swinging fork with coil spring hydraulically damped units.

Electrical Equipment
Generator: Alternator—12 volts.
Batteries: 12 volts 8 A/H lead acid.

Suppression
To F.V.R.D.E. Specification 2051, Appendix D1, Schedule B.

MANUFACTURERS

B.S.A. Motor Cycles Ltd., Armoury Road, Birmingham 11.

3

Motor Cycle (Triumph T50 Services Model)

(Project State—Undergoing User Trials)

Description: This motor cycle is based on the commercial components of the Triumph 5TA model but incorporates features to improve the suitability of the machine for use in a military environment. These features include a special engine air filtration system with a dust-proof carburettor, improved protection for the rear chain and for the front forks. To ensure long life the engine is down rated and a compression ratio of 7 : 1 has been chosen to suit military fuels.

F.V. Specification Number: Chassis 9327.

Height: 3′ 3½″ (*1 m.*).   Length: 6′ 9″ (*2·06 m.*).
Width: 2′ 8″ (*0·81 m.*).   Wheelbase: 4′ 6″ (*1·37 m.*).
Weight: Unladen 382 lb. (*172 kg.*).

PERFORMANCE DATA

Speed, average maximum:
> Road 55 m.p.h. (*88·6 km./h.*).
> C.C. 25 m.p.h. (*40·3 km./h.*).

Range of action at average maximum speed: 250 miles (*403 km.*).
Maximum climbing ability: 1 in 2.

TECHNICAL DATA

Power Unit
Type: Triumph twin cylinder o.h.v.
Displacement: 490 c.c. (30 cu. in.).
Gross B.H.P.: 25 at 6,500 r.p.m.
Nett torque (lb. ft.): 24 at 5,200 r.p.m.
Ignition type: 6 volt coil.

Fuel System
Type: Gravity feed.
Type of fuel: Gasoline.
Air cleaner: Dry—paper element.
Fuel capacity: 3⅜ gallons (*15·3 litres*).

Engine Lubrication
System: Dry sump—plunger type oil pump.

Engine Cooling
System: Air cooled.

Wheels
Front: Rims WM2-19.
Rear: Rims WM3-18.
Front: Tyres 3·00″ × 19″ (universal).
Rear: Tyres 4·00″ × 18″ (trials universal).
Tyre pump: Hand.

Transmission
Clutch: Multi-plate.
Gearbox: 4-speed.
Ratios: Top 6·20: 1. Bottom 19·6 :1.
Final drive: Chain drive to rear wheel.

Brakes
Foot: Mechanical to rear wheel.
Hand: Mechanical to front wheel.

Steering
System: Handlebar.
Turning circle: R.H. 13′ 2″ (*4·01 m.*). L.H. 13′ 8″ (*4·17 m.*).

Suspension
Front: Telescopic—coil spring hydraulically damped.
Rear: Swinging fork with coil spring hydraulically damped units.

Electrical Equipment
Generator: Alternator 12 volts.
Batteries: 12 volts 8 A/H lead acid.
Suppression: To F.V.R.D.E. Specification 2051, Appendix D1, Schedule B.

MANUFACTURERS

TRIUMPH ENGINEERING COMPANY LTD., Allesley, Coventry.

Truck Lightweight Airportable (Austin 4 x 4)

(Project State—Engineering Model)

Description: This vehicle is an experimental prototype designed and built by the British Motor Corporation to meet a General Staff requirement. It embodies the engine, transmission and suspension units of the 1100 range of vehicles. The vehicle body provides accommodation for a driver and three passengers, or, alternatively, a driver and 800 lb. of cargo. Independent suspension is provided on all wheels by means of torsion bars. The engine is transversely mounted at the front of the vehicle with the radiator on the left hand side, with a cowled 'pusher' fan expelling air into the wheel arch. Normal drive is to the front wheels only. Four wheel drive and low range are engaged independently.

Height: 4′ 11″ (*1·5 m.*).   Length: 9′ 3″ (*2·82 m.*).
Width: 4′ 6″ (*1·37 m.*).   Wheelbase: 6′ 5½″ (*1·97 m.*).
Track: Front 3′ 11¼″ (*1·2 m.*).   Rear 3′ 11¾″ (*1·21 m.*).
Weight: Unladen 1,598 lb. (*727 kg.*).   Laden: 2,598 lb. (*1,181 kg.*).

PERFORMANCE DATA

Speed, average maximum (estimated):
    Road 40 m.p.h. (*64 km./h.*).
    C.C. 8–12 m.p.h. (*12·9–19·3 km./h.*).
Range of action at average maximum speed: Approx. 280 miles (road) (*448 km.*).
Gross power weight ratio (b.h.p. per ton): 43.
Maximum tractive effort, low gear (lb. per ton): 1,468.
Maximum climbing ability: 1 in 1·5.
Maximum gradient for stop and restart: 1 in 2.

TECHNICAL DATA

Power Unit
Type: B.M.C., 1100 c.c. gasoline.
Displacement: 1,098 c.c. (67 cu. in.).
Gross b.h.p.: 50 at 5,000 r.p.m.
Nett torque: 60 lb. ft. at 2,500 r.p.m.
Ignition type: Coil, 12 volt.
Fuel System
Type: Electric pump.
Type of fuel: Gasoline.
Air cleaner: Dry, paper element.
Fuel capacity: 8 gallons (*36·4 litres*).
Engine Lubrication
System: Wet sump (combined with transmission).
Engine Cooling
System: Pressurised.
Wheels
Rims: 4″J × 12″.
Tyres: 5·60″ × 12″.
Chains: Non-skid.
Transmission
Clutch: Single dry plate 7⅛″ (*181 mm.*) dia.
Gearbox: 4-speed and reverse.
Transfer box: 2-speed (integral with engine/gearbox unit)
Transfer box ratios: 1 : 1 and 1·64 : 1.
Propeller shaft: To rear axle.

Transmission—*continued*
Axles: Front, helical gear. Rear, spiral gear.
Ratios: Top 4·41 : 1, bottom 26·2 : 1.
Differentials: Two.
Brakes
Foot: Hydraulic (all wheels).
Hand: Mechanical (rear wheels only).
Trailer: Over-run.
Steering
System: Rack and pinion.
Turning circle: R.H. 34′ 7″ (*10·54 metres*). L.H. 34′ 7″ (*10·54 metres*).
Suspension
Front: Independent, torsion bars.
Rear: Independent, torsion bars.
Shock absorbers : Telescopic, hydraulic.
Towing Attachments
Type: Not fitted.
Electrical Equipment
Generator: 12 volt. D.C. 22 amp. (as standard).
Batteries: One, 12 volt 45 amp./h. (as standard).
Suppression: To F.V.R.D.E.
Specification 2051, Appendix D1, Schedule B.

MANUFACTURERS

Chassis: ⎫
Body: ⎭ AUSTIN MOTOR COMPANY LTD., Longbridge, Birmingham.

Truck Cargo Mini (Austin Mini-Moke $\frac{1}{4}$ ton 4 x 2)

(Project State—Vehicle in Service)

Description: This military type pick up embodies the engine transmission and independent suspension units of the 'mini' range of vehicles. The body provides accommodation for a driver and three passengers or, alternatively, a driver and 500 lb. of cargo. The engine is mounted transversely at the front of the vehicle with the radiator mounted on the left hand side with a cowled 'pusher' fan expelling air into the wheel arch. Drive is to the front wheels only via a 4-speed synchromesh gearbox and transmission integral with the engine.

Height: 4′ 8″ (*1·42 m.*).   Length: 10′ 0″ (*3·05 m.*).
Width: 4′ 5½″ (*1·36 m.*).   Wheelbase: 6′ 8″ (*2·03 m.*).
Track: Front 3′ 11¾″ (*1·21 m.*).   Rear 3′ 10⅞″ (*1·19 m.*).
Weight: Unladen 1,329 lb. (*604 kg.*).   Laden 2,029 lb. (*924 kg.*).

PERFORMANCE DATA

Speed, average maximum:
    Road 40 m.p.h. (64 *km./h.*).
    C.C. 5–10 m.p.h. (8–16 *km./h.*).
Range of action at average maximum speed: 240 miles (*384 km.*) on road.
Gross power weight ratio (b.h.p. per ton): 40·6.
Maximum tractive effort, low gear (lb. per ton): 773
Maximum climbing ability: 1 in 2·5.
Maximum gradient for stop and restart: 1 in 3.

TECHNICAL DATA

Power Unit
Type: B.M.C., 850 c.c., gasoline.
Displacement: 840 c.c. (51·7 cu. in.).
Gross b.h.p.: 37 at 5,500 r.p.m.
Nett torque: 44 lb. ft. at 2,900 r.p.m.
Ignition type: Coil, 12 volt.

Fuel System
Type: Electric pump.
Type of fuel: Gasoline.
Air cleaner: Dry, paper element.
Fuel capacity: 6 gallons (*27·3 litres*).

Engine Lubrication
System: Wet sump (combined with transmission).

Engine Cooling
System: Pressurised.

Wheels
Rims: 3·50″ × 10″.
Tyres: 5·20″ × 10″.
Chains: Non-skid.

Transmission
Clutch: Single dry plate.
Gearbox: 4-speed and reverse.
Axle: Helical gear.
Ratios: top 3·769 : 1, bottom 13·7 : 1.

Transmission—*continued*
Differentials: One.

Brakes
Foot: Hydraulic (all wheels).
Hand: Mechanical (rear wheels only).
Trailer: Over-run.

Steering
System: Rack and pinion.
Turning circle: R.H. 32′ (*9·85 metres*). L.H. 31′ 4″ (*9·55 metres*).

Suspension
Front: Independent, rubber compression units.
Rear: Independent, rubber compression units.
Shock absorbers: Telescopic, hydraulic.

Towing Attachments
Type: Rear, none (as standard).

Electrical Equipment
Generator: 12 volt D.C. 22 amp.
Batteries: One, 12 volt 45 amp./h.
Suppression: To F.V.R.D.E. Specification 2051, Appendix D1, Schedule B.

MANUFACTURERS

Chassis:⎫
Body: ⎬ AUSTIN MOTOR COMPANY LTD., Longbridge, Birmingham.

Truck General Service (Rover 8, ¼ ton 4 x 4)
(Project State—In Service)

Description: This vehicle is based on the current commercial specification for the 88″ wheelbase Landrover. Changes to the commercial specification have been made to render the vehicle more acceptable for Service use, these include, reinforced rear cross member and F.V. design towing hook; military pattern divided wheels; tyres with cross-country tread; twin fuel tanks; vehicle lashing eyes at front and rear; freight lashing cleats in body; rear bumpers and modified front bumper to permit pushing of one vehicle by another; oil cooler and eight-bladed fan; F.V. pattern lights, mounting points to accept installation of wireless equipment in an emergency. The electrical system is 12 volt. The vehicle is capable of carrying 900 lb. of cargo, across rough terrain, in addition to the driver and one passenger. Exhibit No. 7 is an identical vehicle fitted with 8·20 × 15 ribbed desert pattern tyres which increases the Maximum Tractive Effort to 2,150 lb./ton and the Turning Circle to 45′ (*13·7 m.*).

F.V. Specification Number: Chassis/Body 9325 Equipment 9281.

Height: 6′ 5″ (*1·96 m.*).   Length: 12′ 5″ (*3·8 m.*).
Width: 5′ 6½″ (*1·69 m.*).   Wheelbase: 7′ 4″ (*2·23 m.*).
Track: Front 4′ 3½″ (*1·31 m.*).   Rear 4′ 3½″ (*1·31 m.*).
Weight: Unladen 3,364 lb. (*1,530 kg.*).   Laden 4,460 lb. (*2,030 kg.*).

PERFORMANCE DATA

Speed, average maximum:
Road 45 m.p.h. (*72·4 km./h.*).   C.C. 12 m.p.h. (*19·3 km/h.*).
Range of action at average maximum speed: 350 miles (*563 km.*).
Gross power weight ratio (b.h.p. per ton): 38·6.
Maximum tractive effort, low gear (lb. per ton): 2·080.
Maximum climbing ability: 1 in 2·75.
Maximum gradient for stop and restart: 1 in 2·75.

TECHNICAL DATA

Power Unit
Type: Rover, 2¼ litre, gasoline.
Displacement: 2,286 c.c. (139 cu. in.).
Gross B.H.P.: 77 at 4,250 r.p.m.
Nett torque: 116 lb. ft. at 1,500 r.p.m.
Ignition type: Coil 12 volt.

Fuel System
Type: Mechanical lift pump.
Type of Fuel: Gasoline.
Air cleaner: Oil bath with pre-cleaner.
Fuel capacity: 20 gallons (Imp.) (*90·86 litres*).

Engine Lubrication
System: Wet sump.

Engine Cooling
System: Pressurised.

Wheels
Rims: 4·50″ E × 16″ W.D. divided type (FV.84919).
Tyres: 6·50″ × 16″—6 P.R. passenger with C.C. tread pattern.
Tyre Pump: Manual.
Chains: Commercial.

Transmission
Clutch: Enclosed S.D.P. 9″ dia. (*0·228 metres*)
Gearbox: 4-speed and reverse (synchromesh on 3rd and 4th gears).
Transfer Box: 2-speed.
Transfer box ratios: 1·148 : 1 and 2·400 : 1.

Transmission—*continued*
Propeller shafts: Telescopic with Hookes couplings.
Axles: Spiral bevel (front and rear).
Ratios: Top, 5·400 : 1, Bottom, 40·600 : 1.
Differentials: Two.

Brakes
Foot: Hydraulic, all wheels, drum type.
Hand: Mechanical, transmission, drum type.

Steering
System: Ackermann.
Turning circle: 42′ max. (*12·8 metres*).

Suspension
Front: Semi-elliptic leaf springs.
Rear: Semi-elliptic leaf springs.
Shock absorbers: Hydraulic, telescopic double-acting type.

Towing Attachments
Type: Front, provision only. Rear, rotating/lockable hook (FV. 332151).

Electrical Equipment
Generator: 12 volt D.C.
Batteries: 12 volt (lead/acid) 51 A.H. capacity.
Suppression: F.V.R.D.E. Specification 2051, Schedule B, Appendix D1.

MANUFACTURERS

Chassis: ⎱ THE ROVER Co. LTD., Meteor Works,
Body: ⎰ Lode Lane, Solihull, Warwickshire.

ALTERNATIVE ROLES

Emergency wireless carrier (without battery charging facilities).
Emergency stretcher carrier.
WOMBAT carrier.
Line Layer.
3·5 kVA Onan generator.
Mortar carrier.

Trailer Cargo ($\frac{3}{4}$ ton)
(Project State—In Service)

Description: This two-wheeled trailer is of $\frac{3}{4}$ ton capacity and is of welded steel construction. The body is water-tight and is capable of floating and shallow water-fording. The trailer is fitted with stabilizing jacks, one at the front and two at the rear. Lashing points are provided for securing the load and for a canvas tilt cover. The size and weight of the trailer allows for airportability in transport aircraft in Service use.

F.V Specification Number: Chassis/Body 9307.

Height: 3′ 1″ (*0·94 m.*).   Length: 9′ 7″ (*2·92 m.*).
Width: 4′ 8″ (*1·425 m.*).
Track: 3′ 11″ (1·2 *m.*).
Weight: Laden 2,464 lb. (*1,120 kg.*).

TECHNICAL DATA

Wheels
Rims: 4·50″ × 16″ 4-stud fixing.
Tyres: 6·50″ × 16″.

Brakes
Service: Over-run mechanical.
Parking: Mechanical connection

Brakes—*continued*
to over-run.

Suspension
Semi-elliptic springs and Aeon rubber.
Shock absorbers: Telescopic hydraulic.

MANUFACTURERS

Chassis: ⎱
Body: ⎰ PRESSED STEEL CO. LTD.

Trailer Tanker Water (100 gall. ¾ ton)

(Project State—In Service)

Description: This trailer is basically an FV.2360 type chassis fitted with a 100 gallon water tank. The tank is of welded steel construction incorporating a large manhole with a hinged cover for access purposes. It is fitted internally with anti-surge baffles and has provision for fitting an immersion heater. Back flushing, draining and filling cocks are provided. A semi-rotary hand pump is provided to fill the tank with filtered water at a maximum rate of 10 gal./minute.

F.V. Specification Number: Chassis 9307. Body 9055. Equipment 9055.

Height: 3′ 1″ (*0·94 m.*).   Length: 9′ 7″ (*2·92 m.*).
Track: 3′ 11″ (*1·2 m.*).
Weight: Unladen 1,240 lb. (*564 kg.*).   Laden 2,240 lb. (*1,020 kg.*).

TECHNICAL DATA

Wheels
Rims: 4·50″E × 16″ 5 stud fitting.
Tyres: 6·50″ × 16″.

Brakes
Service: Over-run mechanical.
Parking: Mechanical connection to over-run.

Suspension
Semi-elliptic springs and Aeon rubber.
Shock absorbers: Telescopic hydraulic.

Towing Attachments
Type: Draught eye.

MANUFACTURERS

Chassis:
Body: } PRESSED STEEL CO. LTD.
Equipment:

Truck General Service F.F.R.
(Rover 8, $\frac{1}{4}$ ton 4 x 4)
(Project State—In Service)

Description: This vehicle is based on the current commercial specification for the 88″ wheelbase Landrover. Changes to the commercial specification have been made to render the vehicle more acceptable for Service use, especially in the radio carrying role, these include, 24 volt 90 amp rectified A.C. electrical system with provision for charging the wireless batteries, full suppression of electrical equipment, built-in equipment for radio role including—wireless table, battery carrier, two 100 A.H. batteries, co-axial aerial leads, H.F. aerial brackets, operator's seat, etc. Other specification changes are as for Exhibit No. 5.

F.V. Specification Number: Chassis/Body 9324. Equipment 9281.

Height: 6′ 5″ (*1·96 m.*).   Length: 12′ 5″ (*3·80 m.*).
Width: 5′ 6½″ (*1·69 m.*). Wheelbase: 7′ 4″ (*2·23 m.*).
Track: Front 4′ 3½″ (*1·31 m.*).   Rear: 4′ 3½″ (*1·31 m.*).
Weight: Unladen (including wireless fittings stated in description of vehicle) 3,748 lb. (*1,700 kg.*). Laden 4,776 lb. (*2,170 kg.*).

PERFORMANCE DATA

Speed, average maximum: Road 45 m.p.h. (*72·4 km./h.*).
    C.C. 12 m.p.h. (*19·3 km./h.*).
Range of action at average maximum speed: 350 miles (*563 km.*).
Gross power weight ratio (b.h.p. per ton): 36·2.
Maximum tractive effort, low gear (lb. per ton): 1,950.
Maximum climbing ability: 1 in 2.75.
Maximum gradient for stop and restart: 1 in 2.75.

TECHNICAL DATA

Power Unit
Type: Rover, $2\frac{1}{4}$ litre, gasoline.
Displacement: 2,286 c.c. (139 cu. in.)
Gross B.H.P.: 77 at 4,250 r.p.m.
Nett torque: 116 lb. ft. at 1,500 r.p.m.
Ignition Type: Coil, 10 volt with resistor.

Fuel System
Type: Mechanical lift pump.
Type of Fuel: Gasoline.
Air cleaner: Oil bath with pre-cleaner.
Fuel capacity: 20 gallons (Imp.) (*90·86 litres*).

Engine Lubrication
System: Wet sump.

Engine Cooling
System: Pressurised.

Wheels
Rims: 4·50″E × 16″ W.D. divided type (FV. 84919).
Tyres: 6·50″ × 16″—6 P.R. passenger C.C.
Tyre Pump: Manual.
Chains: Commercial.

Transmission
Clutch: Enclosed S.D.P. 9″ (*0·228 m.*) dia.
Gearbox: 4-speed and reverse (synchromesh on 3rd and 4th gears).
Transfer box: 2-speed.
Transfer box ratios: 1·148 : 1 and 2·400 : 1.

Propeller shafts: Telescopic with Hookes couplings.
Axles: Spiral bevel (front and rear).
Ratios: Top 5·400 : 1, bottom 40·600 : 1.
Differentials: Two.

Brakes
Foot: Hydraulic, all wheels, drum type.
Hand: Mechanical, transmission, drum type.

Steering
System: Ackermann.
Turning circle: 42′ max. (*12·8 m.*).

Suspension
Front: Semi-elliptic leaf springs.
Rear: Semi-elliptic leaf springs.
Shock absorbers: Hydraulic, telescopic double acting type.

Towing Attachments
Type: Front, provision only. Rear, rotating/lockable hook (F.V.332151).

Electrical Equipment
Generator: 24 volt A.C. with inbuilt Silicon diode rectifiers (90 amps. output).
Batteries: Vehicle, lead/acid 12 volt × 2, 43 A.H. Equipment, lead-acid 12 volt × 2, 100 A.H. (Provision is made for a second pair of batteries where increased capacity is required).
Suppression: Full suppression (F.V.R.D.E. Specification 2051, Schedule A, Appendix D1).

MANUFACTURERS

Chassis: ⎫ THE ROVER CO., LTD., Meteor Works, Lode Lane, Solihull,
Body: ⎭ Warwickshire.

ALTERNATIVE ROLES

Helicopter and light aircraft slave starting.
Electronic installations requiring 24 volts power supply.

Truck General Service (Rover 9, ¾ ton 4 x 4)
(Project State—In Service)

Description: This vehicle is based on the current commercial specification for the 109″ wheelbase Landrover. Changes to the commercial specification have been made to render the vehicle more acceptable for Service use. These differences in specification are as for Exhibit No. 5. In addition the chassis frame has deeper spring attachments to permit fitment of larger tyres when required. The vehicle is capable of carrying ¾ ton of cargo across rough terrain, in addition to the driver and one passenger. The vehicle exhibited is fitted with 9·00 × 15 sand tyres and an Applique two stretcher conversion kit which has been designed for evacuation of casualties from forward areas.

F.V. Specification Number: Chassis/Body 9321/9281.

Height: 6′ 9″ (*2·06 m.*).   Length: 15′ 3″ (*4·65 m.*).
Width: 5′ 6½″ (*1·69 m.*).   Wheelbase: 9′ 1″ (*2·77 m.*).
Track: Front 4′ 3½″ (*1·31 m.*). Rear 4′ 3½″ (*1·31 m.*).
Weight: Unladen 3,686 lb. (*1,680 kg.*).   Laden 5,766 lb. (*2,620 kg.*).

PERFORMANCE DATA

Speed, average maximum:
Road 45 m.p.h. (*72·4 km./h.*).   C.C. 10 m.p.h. (*16·09 km./h.*).
Range of action at average maximum speed: 280 miles (*450 km.*).
Gross power weight ratio (b.h.p. per ton): 29·2.
Maximum tractive effort, low gear (lb. per ton): 1,505.
Maximum climbing ability: better than 1 in 3.
Maximum gradient for stop and restart: 1 in 3.

TECHNICAL DATA

Power Unit
Type: Rover, 2¼ litre, gasoline.
Displacement: 2,286 c.c. (139 cu. in.).
Gross: B.H.P.: 77 at 4,250 r.p.m.
Nett Torque: 116 lb. ft. at 1,500 r.p.m.
Ignition type: Coil, 12 volt.
Fuel System
Type: Mechanical lift pump.
Type of Fuel: Gasoline.
Air cleaner: Oil bath with pre-cleaner.
Fuel capacity: 20 gallons (Imp.) (*90·86 litres*).
Engine Lubrication
System: Wet sump.
Engine Cooling
System: Pressurised.
Wheels
Rims: 5·50″E × 16″ W.D. divided type (FV. 84930).
Tyres: 7·50″ × 16″—6 P.R. Light Truck C.C.
(As Exhibited: Rims, 6L × 15″ W/BR pattern Tyres 9·00″ × 15″ ribbed desert pattern).
Tyre pump: Manual.
Chains: Commercial.
Transmission
Clutch: Enclosed S.D.P. 9″ (*0·228 metres*) diameter.
Gearbox: 4-speed and reverse (synchromesh on 3rd and 4th gears).

Transfer box: 2-speed.
Transfer box ratios: 1·148 : 1 and 2·400 : 1.
Propeller shafts: Telescopic with Hookes couplings.
Axles: Spiral bevel (front and rear).
Ratios: Top, 5·400 : 1, bottom 40·600 : 1.
Differentials: Two.
Brakes
Foot: Hydraulic, all wheels, drum type.
Hand: Mechanical, transmission, drum type.
Steering
System: Ackermann.
Turning circle: 50′ max. (*15·25 metres*).
Suspension
Front: Semi-elliptic leaf springs.
Rear: Semi-elliptic leaf springs.
Shock absorbers: Hydraulic, telescopic double acting type.
Towing Attachments
Type: Front, provision only. rear, rotating/lockable hook (F.V.332151).
Electrical Equipment
Generator: 12 volt D.C.
Batteries: 12 volt (lead/acid) 51 A.H. capacity.
Suppression: F.V.R.D.E. Specification 2051, Schedule B, Appendix D1.

MANUFACTURERS

Chassis: } The Rover Co. Ltd., Meteor Works,
Body: Lode Lane, Solihull, Warwickshire.

ALTERNATIVE ROLES

Emergency wireless carrier (without battery charging facilities).
Emergency stretcher carrier.
Wombat carrier.

Truck General Service/G.W.
(Rover 9, $\frac{3}{4}$ ton 4 x 4)

Description: This exhibit shows a simple traversable launcher designed to fire Vigilant (the anti tank missile) from Landrover.

The launcher consists of a traversable centre section, with two missiles in the ready to fire position. This arrangement is mounted on a welded frame which carries three spare missiles. Further spare missiles may be carried in the vehicle aft of driver and passengers accommodation.

Firing can be carried out remote from the vehicle by using a combined sight/controller and a separation cable.

The vehicle is similar to Exhibit No. 10.

Minimal modification is required to the vehicle to fire the guided weapon installation.

MANUFACTURER

Vehicle: THE ROVER CO. LTD.
Guided Weapon System: BRITISH AIRCRAFT CORPORATION.

Truck General Service F.F.R.
(Rover 9, ¾ ton 4 x 4)
(Project State—In Service)

Description: This vehicle is based on the current commercial specification for the 109″ wheelbase Landrover. Changes to the commercial specification have been made to render the vehicle more acceptable for Service use, especially in the radio carrying role, these include 24 volt 90 amp rectified A.C. electrical system with provision for charging the wireless batteries, full suppression of electrical equipment, built-in equipment for radio role including: wireless table, battery carrier, two 100 A.H. batteries, co-axial aerial leads, HF aerial brackets, two operators' seats, etc. Other specification changes are as for Exhibit No. 5.

F.V. Specification Number: Chassis/Body 9322. Equipment: 9281.

Height: 6′ 9″ (*2·06 m.*).   Length: 15′ 3″ (*4·65 m.*).
Width: 5′ 6½″ (*1·69 m.*).   Wheelbase: 9′ 1″ (*2·77 m.*).
Track: Front 4′ 3½″ (*1·31 m.*).   Rear 4′ 3½″ (*1·31 m.*).
Weight: Unladen 4,129 lb. (*1,875 kg.*) (including radio fittings stated in description).   Laden 5,733 lb. (*2,600 kg.*).

PERFORMANCE DATA

Speed, average maximum: Road 45 m.p.h. (*72·4 km./h.*).
C.C. 10 m.p.h. (*16·09 km./h.*).
Range of action at average maximum speed: 280 miles (*450 km.*).
Gross power weight ratio (b.h.p. per ton): 30·1.
Maximum tractive effort, low gear (lb. per ton): 1,515.
Maximum climbing ability: 1 in 3.
Maximum gradient for stop and restart: 1 in 3.

TECHNICAL DATA

Power Unit
Type: Rover, $2\frac{1}{4}$ litre gasoline.
Displacement: 2,286 c.c. (139 cu. in.).
Gross B.H.P.: 77 at 4,250 r.p.m.
Nett Torque: 116 lb. ft. at 1,500 r.p.m.
Ignition Type: Coil, 10 volt with resistor.

Fuel System
Type: Mechanical lift pump.
Type of Fuel: Gasoline.
Air cleaner: Oil bath with pre-cleaner.
Fuel capacity: 20 gallons (Imp.) (*90·86 litres*).

Engine Lubrication
System: Wet sump.

Engine Cooling
System: Pressurised.

Wheels
Rims: 5·50″E × 16″ W.D. divided type 84930.
Tyres: 7·50″ × 16″—6 P.R. C.C.
Tyre Pump: Manual.
Chains: Commercial.

Transmission
Clutch: Enclosed S.D.P. 9″ (*0·228 metres*) diameter.
Gearbox: 4-speed and reverse (synchromesh on 3rd and 4th gears).
Transfer box: 2-speed.
Transfer box ratios: 1·148 : 1 and 2·400 : 1.
Propeller shafts: Telescopic with Hookes couplings.

Axles: Spiral bevel (front and rear).
Ratios: Top: 5·400 : 1, bottom 40·600 : 1.
Differentials: Two.

Brakes
Foot: Hydraulic, all wheels, drum type.
Hand: Mechanical, transmission, drum type.

Steering
System: Ackermann.
Turning circle: 50′ max. (*15·25 metres*).

Suspension
Front: Semi-elliptic leaf springs.
Rear: Semi-elliptic leaf springs.
Shock absorbers: Hydraulic, telescopic, double acting.

Towing Attachments
Type: Front, provision only. Rear, rotating/lockable hook (F.V. 332151).

Electrical Equipment
Generator: 24 volt A.C. with inbuilt silicon diode rectifiers (90 amps output).
Batteries: Vehicle, lead/acid 12 volt × 2, 43 A.H.
Equipment: Lead/acid 12 volt × 2, 100 A.H. (provision is made for a second pair of batteries when increased capacity is required).
Suppression: Full suppression (F.V.R.D.E. Specification 2051, Schedule A, Appendix D1).

MANUFACTURERS

Chassis: ⎱ The Rover Co. Ltd., Meteor Works,
Body: ⎰ Lode Lane, Solihull, Warwickshire.

ALTERNATIVE ROLES

Helicopter and light aircraft slave starting. Electronic installations requiring 24 volts power supply.

Truck General Service (Rover ½ ton Diesel)
(Project State—In Service)

Description: This is a 109″ wheelbase Landrover fitted with a hard top. The vehicle is diesel powered and has a flame trap and spark arrester in lieu of a silencer. A 12 volt a.c. alternator has been substituted for the normal electrical system, to provide power for the radio installation.

Height: 6′ 6″ (*1·98 m.*).   Length: 15′ 3″ (*4·65 m.*).
Width: 5′ 5½″ (*1·66 m.*).   Wheelbase: 9′ 1″ (*2·77 m.*).
Track: Front 4′ 3½″ (*1·31 m.*).   Rear 4′ 3½″ (*1·31 m.*).
Weight: Unladen 3,471 lb. (*1,574 kg.*).   Laden 5,181 lb. (*2,349·5 kg.*).

PERFORMANCE DATA

Speed, average maximum:
    Road 45 m.p.h. (*72·4 km./h.*).   C.C. 15 m.p.h. (*24·3 km./h.*).
Range of action at average maximum speed: 280 miles (*560 km.*).
Gross power weight ratio (b.h.p. per ton): 29·6.
Maximum tractive effort, low gear (lb. per ton): 1,380.

TECHNICAL DATA

Power Unit
Type: Rover, 2¼ litre, Diesel.
Displacement: 2,286 c.c. (*139 cu. ins.*).
Gross B.H.P.: 68 at 4,000 r.p.m.
Nett torque: 103 lb. ft. at 1,800 r.p.m.
Ignition type: Compression.

Fuel System
Type: C.A.V. D.P.A. fuel injection pump with mechanical governor and pintaux type injectors.
Type of fuel: Diesel.
Air cleaner: Oil bath type.
Fuel capacity: 10 gallons (*45·5 litres*).

Engine Lubrication
System: Wet sump.

Engine Cooling
System: Pressurised.

Wheels
Rims: Divided wheels.
Tyres: 700 × 16

Transmission
Clutch: 9″ single dry plate.
Gearbox: 4-speed and reverse.
Transfer box: Two-speed.
Propeller Shafts: Hardy Spicer.

Transmission—*continued*
Axles: Fully floating with spiral bevel drive.
Ratios: Top 5·4 : 1, bottom 40·6 : 1.
Differentials: Two.

Brakes
Foot: Girling hydraulic.
Hand: Internal expanding transmission type.

Steering
System: Burman worm and nut with recirculating ball.
Turning circle: R.H. 47′ (*14·3 metres*). L.H. 47′ (*14·3 metres*).

Suspension
Front: Semi-elliptic springs.
Rear: Semi-elliptic springs.
Shock absorbers: Telescopic type front and rear.

Towing Attachments
Type: Front, single hook. Rear, multi hitch 4 position.

Electrical Equipment
Generator: 12 volt a.c. rectified.
Batteries: 38 amp./h. 12 volt.
Suppression: To F.V.R.D.E. Specification 2051, Appendix D1, Schedule B.

MANUFACTURERS

Chassis: ⎱
Body: ⎰ ROVER LTD., Solihull.

Truck General Service Lightweight
(Rover Mk. 1, $\frac{1}{4}$ ton 4 x 4)
(Project State—Still Under Development)

Description: This vehicle has been developed to meet a General Staff requirement for a lightweight airportable, helicopter liftable vehicle, having a useful payload and capable of towing light support weapons. The vehicle is based on the existing in Service Truck Exhibit No. 5, having power unit, transmission, suspension, brakes and steering in common. The main difference between the vehicles is in regard to body construction, which has been designed to meet the same roles as the existing vehicle and offering a similar degree of weather protection, see Exhibit No. 14. It is also capable of being reduced in weight and bulk to a greater extent for air transportation and helicopter lifting, resulting in a stark but useful vehicle as exhibited weighing approximately 2,500 lb. The vehicle is capable of carrying a payload of 896 lb. plus driver and one passenger. This exhibit is fitted with 8·20 × 15 ribbed desert pattern tyres.

Height: 4' 10" (*1·48 m.*).   Length: 11' 11" (*3·63 m.*).
Width: 5' 0" (*1·52 m.*).   Wheelbase: 7' 4" (*2·23 m.*).
Track: Front 4' 3½" (*1·31 m.*).   Rear 4' 3½" (*1·31 m.*).
Weight: Unladen (with 20 gall. fuel) 3,100 lb. (*1,406 kg.*)   Laden 4,396 lb. (*1,995 kg.*).

PERFORMANCE DATA (on standard tyres)

Speed, average maximum:
     Road 45 m.p.h. (*72·4 km./h.*).
     C.C. 12 m.p.h. (*19·3 km./h.*).
Range of action at average maximum speed: 350 miles (*563 km.*).
Gross power weight ratio (b.h.p. per ton): 41·4.
Maximum tractive effort, low gear (lb. per ton): 2,230.
Maximum climbing ability: 1 in 2·75.
Maximum gradient for stop and restart: 1 in 2·75.

TECHNICAL DATA

Power Unit
Type: Rover, 2¼ litre, gasoline.
Displacement: 2,286 c.c. (139 cu. in.).
Gross B.H.P.: 77 at 4,250 r.p.m.
Nett torque: 116 lb. ft. at 1,500 r.p.m.
Ignition type: Coil, 12 volt.
Fuel System
Type: Mechanical lift pump.
Type of fuel: Gasoline.
Air cleaner: Oil bath with pre-cleaner.
Fuel capacity: 20 gallons (Imp.)
(*90·86 litres*).
Engine Lubrication
System: Wet sump.
Engine Cooling
System: Pressurised.
Wheels
Rims: 5·00″ F × 16″ commercial—
well based.
Tyres: 6·50″ × 16″—6 P.R. C.C.
Tyre pump: Manual.
Chains: Commercial.
Transmission
Clutch: Enclosed 9″ (*0·228 metres*)
dia. S.D.P.
Gearbox: 4-speed and reverse (synchromesh on 3rd and 4th gears).
Transfer box: 2-speed.
Transfer box ratios: 1·148 : 1 and
2·400 : 1.

Transmission—*continued*
Propeller shafts: Telescopic with
Hookes couplings.
Axles: Spiral bevel (front and rear).
Ratios: Top 5·400 : 1, bottom
40·600 : 1.
Differentials: Two.
Brakes
Foot: Hydraulic, all wheel, drum
type.
Hand: Mechanical, transmission,
drum type.
Steering
System: Ackermann.
Turning circle: 42′ max. (*12·8 metres*).
Suspension
Front: Semi-elliptic leaf springs.
Rear: Semi-elliptic leaf springs.
Shock absorbers: Hydraulic, telescopic double acting.
Towing Attachments
Type: Front, provision only. Rear,
rotating/lockable hook (FV.332151).
Electrical Equipment
Generator: 12 volt D.C.
Batteries: 12 volt (lead/acid) 51 A.H.
capacity.
Suppression: F.V.R.D.E.
Specification 2051. Schedule B,
Appendix D1.

MANUFACTURERS

Chassis: ⎱ THE ROVER CO. LTD., Meteor Works,
Body: ⎰ Lode Lane, Solihull, Warwickshire.

ALTERNATIVE ROLES

Emergency wireless carrier (without battery charging facilities).
Emergency stretcher carrier.

Truck General Service Lightweight FFR
(Rover Mk. 1, $\frac{1}{4}$ ton 4 x 4)
(Project State—Still under Development)

Description: This vehicle is the radio carrying version of Exhibit No. 13. The vehicle has identical charging and radio installation facilities to those in Exhibit No. 9.

Height: 6′ 5″ (*1·96 m.*).   Length: 12′ 3″ (*3·73 m.*).
Width: 5′ 3¾″ (*1·62 m.*).   Wheelbase: 7′ 4″ (*2·23 m.*).
Track: Front 4′ 3½″ (*1·31 m.*).   Rear: 4′ 3½″ (*1·31 m.*).
Weight: Unladen (with 20 galls. fuel and wireless fittings but no sets) 3,514 lb. (*1,600 kg.*)   Laden 4,396 lb. (*1,995 kg.*).

PERFORMANCE DATA

Speed, average maximum:
    Road 45 m.p.h. (*72·4 km./h.*).   C.C. 12 m.p.h. (*19·3 km./h.*).
Range of action at average maximum speed: 350 miles (*563 km.*).
Gross power weight ratio (b.h.p. per ton): (a) 43·5. (b) 39·9.
Maximum tractive effort, low gear (lb. per ton): (a) 2,350. (b) 2,150.
Maximum climbing ability: Better than 1 in 2·75.
Maximum gradient for stop and restart: Better than 1 in 2·75.

TECHNICAL DATA

Power Unit
Type: Rover, 2¼ litre, gasoline.
Displacement: 2,286 c.c. (139 cu. in.).
Gross B.H.P.: 77 at 4,250 r.p.m.
Nett torque: 116 lb. ft. at 1,500 r.p.m.
Ignition type: Coil, 10 volts with resistor.

Fuel System
Type: Mechanical lift pump.
Type of Fuel: Gasoline.
Air cleaner: Oil bath with pre-cleaner.
Fuel capacity: 20 gallons (Imp.) (*90.86 litres*).

Engine Lubrication
System: Wet sump.

Engine Cooling
System: Pressurised.

Wheels
Rims: 5·00″F × 16″ commercial wellbased.
Tyres: 6·50″ × 16″ 6 P.R. Passenger C.C.
Tyre pump: Manual.
Chains: Commercial.

Transmission
Clutch: Enclosed S.D.P. 9″ (*0·228 metres*) dia.
Gearbox: 4-speed and reverse. (synchromesh on 3rd and 4th gears).
Transfer box: 2-speed.
Transfer box ratios: 1·148 : 1 and 2·400 : 1.
Propeller shafts: Telescopic with Hookes couplings.

Transmission—*continued*
Axles: Spiral bevel (front and rear).
Ratios: top 5·400 : 1, bottom 40·600 : 1.
Differentials: Two.

Brakes
System: Hydraulic, all wheels, drum type.
Hand: Mechanical, transmission, drum type.

Steering
System: Ackermann.
Turning circle: 42′ max. (*12·8 metres*).

Suspension
Front: Semi-elliptic leaf springs.
Rear: Semi-elliptic leaf springs.
Shock absorbers: Hydraulic, telescopic, double acting.

Towing Attachments
Type: Front, provision only. Rear, rotating/lockable hook (F.V.332151).

Electrical Equipment
Generator: 24 volt A.C. with inbuilt Silicon diode rectifiers (90 amps. output).
Batteries: Vehicle, lead-acid, 2 × 23 volt 43 A.H. Equipment, lead/acid, 2 × 12 volt, 100 A.H. (provision is made for a second pair of batteries where increased capacity is required).
Suppression: Full suppression (F.V.R.D.E. Specification 2051, Schedule A, Appendix D1).

MANUFACTURERS

Chassis: ⎰ THE ROVER CO. LTD., Meteor Works, Lode Lane, Solihull,
Body: ⎱ Warwickshire.

ALTERNATIVE ROLES

None contemplated at this stage of development but vehicle could be used for electronic installation requiring 24 volts power supply.

Truck Cargo (Rover ¾ ton) and Trailer Cargo (Scottorn ¾ ton) Power Driven Train
(Project State—Under Assessment)

Description: The short wheelbase Landrover and driven axle Scottorn trailer are available commercially. This long wheelbase vehicle and trailer train have been prototyped for technical assessment in aid of a M.O.D. (R.A.F.) requirement for a light tactical airportable fire appliance and for research. The basic vehicle is [to F.V.R.D.E. Specification 9322 and is similar to Exhibit No. 11 but with an additional transfer box at the rear of the vehicle, coupled to the power take-off on the main gearbox to provide the driving facility for the trailer. The trailer is fitted with a driving axle basically common to the rear axle on the vehicle. Drive from the vehicle to the trailer axle is by means of two telescopic tubular propeller shafts with single Hookes type universal joints. The shaft coupling the trailer to the vehicle drive is quickly detachable.

Height: 6′ 9″ (*2·06 m.*).   Length: 24′ 8″ (*7·46 m.*).
Width: 5′ 6½″ (*1·69 m.*).   Wheelbase: 9′ 1″ (*2·77 m.*).
Track: Front 4′ 3½″ (*1·31 m.*).   Rear 4′ 3½″ (*1·31 m.*).
Weight: Unladen 4,476 lb. (*2,030 kg.*).   Laden: 8,796 lb. (*4,000 kg.*).

PERFORMANCE DATA

Speed, average maximum:
    Road 45 m.p.h. (*72·4 km./h.*).
    C.C. 10 m.p.h. (*16·09 km./h.*).
Range of action at average maximum speed: 250 miles (*403 km.*).
Gross power weight ratio (b.h.p. per ton): 19·6.
Maximum tractive effort, low gear (lb. per ton): 987.
Maximum climbing ability: 1 in 3.
Maximum gradient for stop and restart: 1 in 3.

TECHNICAL DATA

Power Unit
Type: Rover, 2¼ litre, gasoline.
Displacement: 2,286 c.c. (139 cu. in.).
Gross B.H.P.: 77 at 4,250 r.p.m.
Nett torque: 116 lb. ft. at 1,500 r.p.m.
Ignition type: Coil 10 volt with resistor.
Fuel System
Type: Mechanical lift pump.
Type of fuel: Petrol.
Air cleaner: Oil bath with pre-cleaner.
Fuel capacity: 20 gallons (Imp.) (*90·86 litres*).
Engine Lubrication
System: Wet sump.
Engine Cooling
System: Pressurised
Wheels
Rims: Vehicle and Trailer: 5·50″E × 16″ W.D. divided type (FV. 84930).
Tyres: Vehicle and Trailer: 7·50″ × 16″ 6 P.R. Light truck C.C.
Tyre Pump: Manual.
Chains: Commercial.
Transmission
Clutch: Enclosed S.D.P. 9″ (*0·228 m.*) diameter.
Gearbox: 4-speed and reverse (synchromesh on 3rd and 4th gears).
Transfer box: 2-speed.
Transfer box ratios: 1·148 : 1 and 2·400 : 1.
Propeller shafts: Telescopic with Hookes couplings.

Transmission—*continued*
Axles: Spiral bevel vehicle (front and rear) and trailer.
Ratios: Top 5·400 : 1, bottom 40·600 : 1.
Differentials: Three.
Brakes
Foot: Vehicle: Hydraulic, drum type.
Foot: Trailer: Over-run, drum type.
Hand: Vehicle: Mechanical, transmission, drum type.
Hand: Trailer: Mechanical, drum type.
Steering
System: Ackermann.
Turning circle: 50′ max. (*15·25 m.*).
Suspension
Front: Semi-elliptic leaf springs.
Rear: Semi-elliptic leaf springs.
Trailer: Semi-elliptic leaf springs with Aeon rubber springs.
Shock absorbers: Vehicle, hydraulic, telescopic double acting. Trailer, hydraulic, telescopic double acting.
Towing Attachments
Type: Front, provision only. Rear, rotating/lockable hook (FV.332151).
Electrical Equipment
Generator: 24 A.C. with in-built rectifier (90 amps. output).
Batteries: Two × 12 volt 43 A.H. capacity (lead/acid).
Suppression: Full suppression (F.V.R.D.E. Specification 2051, Schedule A, Appendix D1).

MANUFACTURERS

Vehicle: THE ROVER CO. LTD., in conjunction with
Trailer; SCOTTORN LTD.

Truck General Service Line Layer
(Rover 8, $\frac{1}{4}$ ton 4 x 4)

(Project State—In Service)

Description: This vehicle is similar to Exhibit No. 5, but has been modified to meet a requirement for a light line laying vehicle, by the fitment of an applique kit of parts which has been developed by S.R.D.E.

F.V. Specification Number: Chassis/Body 9325/9281. Equipment: S.R.D.E. Specification.

Height (over structure only): 7′ 7″ (*2·31 m.*).   Length: 12′ 5″ (*3·8 m.*).
Width: 5′ 8″ (*1·73 m.*).   Wheelbase: 7′ 4″ (*2·23 m.*).
Track: Front 4′ 3½″ (*1·31 m.*).   Rear: 4′ 3½″ (*1·31 m.*).
Weight: Unladen 3,364 lb. Basic vehicle weight (*1,530 kg.*). Laden: 4,460 lb. (*2,030 kg.*).

PERFORMANCE DATA

Speed, average maximum:
    Road 45 m.p.h. (*72·4 km./h.*).
    C.C. 12 m.p.h. (*19·3 km./h.*).
Range of action at average maximum speed: 350 miles (563 *km.*).
Gross power weight ratio (b.h.p. per ton): 38·6.
Maximum tractive effort, low gear (lb. per ton): 2,080.
Maximum climbing ability: 1 in 2·75.
Maximum gradient for stop and restart: 1 in 2·75.

TECHNICAL DATA

Power Unit
Type:, Rover, 2¼ litre, gasoline.
Displacement: 2,286 c.c. (139 cu. in.).
Gross B.H.P.: 77 at 4,250 r.p.m.
Nett torque: 116 lb. ft. at 1,500 r.p.m.
Ignition type: Coil, 12 volt.

Fuel System
Type: Mechanical lift pump.
Type of fuel: Gasoline.
Air cleaner: Oil bath with pre-cleaner.
Fuel capacity: 20 gallons (Imp.) (*90·86 litres*).

Engine Lubrication
System: Wet sump.

Engine Cooling
System: Pressurised.

Wheels
Rims: 4·50″E × 16″ W.D. divided type (FV.84919).
Tyres: 6·50″ × 16″ 6 P.R. passenger. C.C.
Tyre pump: Manual.
Chains: Commercial.

Transmission
Clutch: Enclosed S.D.P. 9″ (*0·228 m.*) diameter.
Gearbox: 4-speed and reverse (synchromesh on 3rd and 4th gears).
Transfer box: 2-speed.

Transmission—*continued*
Transfer box ratios: 1·148 : 1 and 2·400 : 1.
Propeller shafts: Telescopic with Hookes couplings.
Axles: Spiral bevel (front and rear).
Ratios: Top 5·400 : 1, bottom 40·600 : 1.
Differentials: Two.

Brakes
Foot: Hydraulic, all wheel, drum type.
Hand: Mechanical, transmission, drum type.

Steering
System: Ackermann.
Turning circle: 42′ max. (*12·8 m.*).

Suspension
Front: Semi-elliptic leaf springs.
Rear: Semi-elliptic leaf springs.
Shock absorbers: Hydraulic, telescopic, double acting.

Towing Attachments
Type: Front, provision only. Rear, rotating/lockable hook (FV.332151).

Electrical Equipment
Generator: 12 volt D.C.
Batteries: 12 volt (lead/acid) 51 A.H. capacity.
Suppression:
F.V.R.D.E. Specification 2051, Schedule B, Appendix D1.

MANUFACTURERS

Chassis:
Body: } THE ROVER CO. LTD.
Equipment: PARK ROYAL VEHICLES, LTD.

Ambulance 2/4 Stretcher
(Rover 9, ¾ ton 4 x 4)
(Project State—In Service)

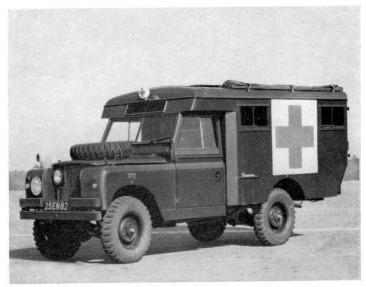

Description: This vehicle has been developed to meet the requirements M.O.D. (Army Dept.) for a small ambulance suitable for evacuation of casualties from forward areas, offering greater comfort than stretcher kits previously carried in jeep-type vehicles. The chassis is based on the current commercial long wheelbase Landrover specification. Changes have been introduced to render the vehicle more suitable for Service use. These include such items as W.D. pattern divided wheels, tyres with C.C. tread pattern, twin fuel tanks, oil cooler and eight bladed fan, F.V. pattern lights modified suspension to improve riding and handling characteristics. The body which is framed and panelled in aluminium is thermally insulated and offers accommodation for a medical attendant and 2 or 4 stretcher cases or alternatively 1 or 2 stretcher cases and 3 sitting patients or 6 sitting cases in addition to the driver. Cab and body ventilation and heating is provided.

F.V. Specification Number: Chassis 9336. Body 9696.

Height: 7′ 0½″ (*2·15 m.*).   Length: 15′ 10″ (*4·83 m.*).
Width: 6′ 3″ (*1·90 m.*).   Wheelbase: 9′ 1″ (*2·77 m.*).
Track: Front 4′ 3½″ (*1·31 m.*).   Rear 4′ 3½″ (*1·31 m.*).

Weight: Unladen 4,256 lb. (*1,930 kg.*). Laden 5,885 lb. (*2,670 kg.*).

PERFORMANCE DATA

Speed, average maximum: Road 45 m.p.h. (*72·4 km./h.*).

C.C. 10 m.p.h. (*16·09 km./h.*).

Range of action at average maximum speed: 280 miles (*450 km.*).

Gross power weight ratio (b.h.p. per ton): 35·3.

Maximum Tractive effort, low gear (lb. per ton): 1,780.

Maximum climbing ability: 1 in 3.

Maximum gradient for stop and restart: 1 in 3.

TECHNICAL DATA

Power Unit

Type: Rover 2¼ litre gasoline.

Displacement: 2,286 c.c. (139 cu. in.).

Gross B.H.P.: 77 at 4,250 r.p.m.

Nett torque: 116 lb. ft. at 1,500 r.p.m.

Ignition type: Coil, 12 volt.

Fuel System

Type: Mechanical lift pump.

Type of fuel: Gasoline.

Air cleaner: Oil bath with pre-cleaner.

Fuel capacity: 20 gallons (Imp.) (*90·86 litres*).

Engine Lubrication

System: Wet sump.

Engine Cooling

System: Pressurised.

Wheels

Rims: 5·50″E × 16″ W.D. divided type (F.V.84930).

Tyres: 7·50″ × 16″, 6 P.R. light truck with C.C. tread pattern.

Tyre pump: Manual.

Chains: Commercial.

Transmission

Clutch: Enclosed S.D.P. 9″ (*·228 metres*) dia.

Gearbox: 4-speed and reverse (synchromesh on 3rd and 4th gears).

Transfer box: 2-speed.

Transfer box ratios: 1·148 : 1 and 2·400 : 1.

Propeller shafts: Telescopic with Hookes couplings.

Axles: Spiral bevel (front and rear).

Ratios: Top 5·400 : 1, bottom 40·600 : 1.

Differentials: Two.

Brakes

Foot: Hydraulic, all wheels, drum type.

Hand: Mechanical, transmission, drum type.

Steering

System: Ackermann.

Turning circle: 50′ max. (*15·25 m.*).

Suspension

Front: Semi-elliptic leaf springs.

Rear: Semi-elliptic leaf springs.

Shock absorbers: Hydraulic, telescopic double acting type.

Electrical Equipment

Generator: 12 volt D.C.

Batteries: 12 volt (lead/acid) 51 A.H. capacity.

Suppression: F.V.R.D.E. Specification 2051, Schedule B, Appendix D1.

MANUFACTURERS

Chassis: THE ROVER CO. LTD., Meteor Works, Lode Lane, Solihull, Warwickshire.

Body: MICKLEOVER TRANSPORT CO. LTD., Park Road, London, N.W.10.

MARSHALL OF CAMBRIDGE (ENGINEERING) LTD., Cambridge.

ALTERNATIVE ROLES

Similar model also used by M.O.D. (R.A.F.).

Truck General Service
(Austin Gipsy ¼ ton 4 x 4)

(Project State—User Trials)

Description: This vehicle is based on the current commercial Gipsy Mk. 4 short wheelbase specification. Changes to the commercial specification have been made to render the vehicle more acceptable for Service use. These include, reinforced rear cross member and military pattern towing hook, military pattern divided wheels and tyres with C.C. tread, twin fuel tanks, vehicle lashing eyes at front and rear, freight lashing cleats in body, rear bumpers and modified front bumpers to permit pushing of one vehicle by another, oil cooler and six bladed fan, F.V. pattern lights, mounting points to accept installation of wireless equipment in emergency. The vehicle is capable of carrying 8 cwt. of load in addition to the driver and one passenger over rough terrain.

F.V. Specification Number: Chassis/Body 9333.

Height: 6′ 5″ (*1·95 m.*). Length: 12′ 2¾″ (*3·72 m.*).
Width: 5′ 6½″ (*1·69 m.*). Wheelbase: 7′ 6″ (*2·29 m.*).
Track: Front 4′ 8⅛″ (*1·42 m.*). Rear 4′ 7⅛″ (*1·4 m.*).
Weight: Unladen 3,448 lb. (*1,570 kg.*). Laden 4,744 lb. (*2,150 kg.*).

PERFORMANCE DATA

Speed, average maximum:
   Road 45 m.p.h. (*72·4 km./h.*). C.C. 10 m.p.h. (*16·09 km./h.*).
Range of action at average maximum speed: 340 miles (*546 km.*).
Gross Power weight ratio (b.h.p. per ton): 33.
Maximum tractive effort, low gear (lb. per ton): 2,075.
Maximum climbing ability: 1 in 2·75.
Maximum gradient for stop and restart: 1 in 2·75.

TECHNICAL DATA

Power Unit
Type: B.M.C., 2·2 litre, gasoline (22 NA).
Displacement: 2,199 c.c. (134·2 cu. in.).
Gross B.H.P.: 70 at 4,000 r.p.m.
Nett torque: 114 lb. ft. at 1,500 r.p.m.
Ignition type: Coil, 12 volt.
Fuel System
Type: Mechanical lift pump.
Type of fuel: Gasoline.
Air cleaner: Oil bath.
Fuel capacity: 20 gallons (Imp.) (*90·86 litres*).
Engine Lubrication
System: Wet sump.
Engine Cooling
System: Pressurised.
Wheels
Rims: 4·50″E × 16″ W.D. divided type (F.V. 84919).
Tyres: 6·50″ × 16″ 6 PR C.C. tread.
Tyre pump: Manual.
Chains: Commercial.
Transmission
Clutch: Enclosed 9″ dia. (*0·228 metres*) S.D.P.
Gearbox: 4-speed synchromesh and reverse.
Transfer box: 2-speed.

Transfer box ratios: 1 : 1 and 2·02 : 1.
Propeller shafts: Telescopic with Hookes couplings.
Axles: Hypoid bevel.
Ratios: Top 5·125 : 1, bottom 41·927 : 1.
Differentials: Two
Brakes
Foot: Hydraulic, all wheels, drum type.
Hand: Mechanical, on rear wheels.
Steering
System: Ackermann.
Turning circle: 42′ max. (12·8 *metres*).
Suspension
Front: Semi-elliptic leaf springs.
Rear: Semi-elliptic leaf springs.
Shock absorbers: Front hydraulic, telescopic double acting. Rear hydraulic, lever type, double acting.
Towing Attachments
Type: Front, provision only. Rear, rotating/lockable hook (F.V.332151).
Electrical Equipment
Generator: 12 volt d.c.
Batteries: 12 volt (lead/acid) 57 A.H.
Suppression: To F.V.R.D.E. Specification 2051, Schedule B, Appendix D1.

MANUFACTURERS

Chassis: ⎱ BRITISH MOTOR CORPORATION (AUSTIN OR MORRIS),
Body: ⎰ Longbridge, Birmingham.

ALTERNATIVE ROLES

Emergency wireless carrier (without battery charging facilities).
Emergency stretcher carrier.

Truck General Service
(Austin Gipsy ¾ ton 4 x 4)
(Project State—User Trials)

Description: This vehicle is based on the current commercial Gipsy Mk. 4 long wheelbase specification. Changes to the commercial specification have been made to render the vehicle more acceptable for Service use. These design changes are as detailed for Exhibit No. 18. This vehicle is capable of carrying ¾ ton of cargo, in addition to the driver and one passenger, over rough terrain.

F.V. Specification Number: Chassis/Body 9334.

Height: 6′ 5½″ (*1·96 m.*).   Length: 13′ 11¾″ (*4·23 m.*).
Width: 5′ 6½″ (*1·69 m.*).   Wheelbase: 9′ 3″ (*2·82 m.*).
Track: Front 4′ 8⅛″ (*1·42 m.*).   Rear 4′ 7⅛″ (*1·4 m.*).
Weight: Unladen 3,664 lb. (*1,670 kg.*).   Laden 5,744 lb. (*2·610 kg.*).

PERFORMANCE DATA

Speed, average maximum:
    Road 45 m.p.h. (*72·4 km./h.*).
    C.C. 10 m.p.h. (*16·09 km./h.*).
Range of action at average maximum speed: 280 miles (*450 km.*).
Gross power weight ratio (b.h.p. per ton): 27·4.
Maximum tractive effort, low gear (lb. per ton): 1,600.
Maximum climbing ability: 1 in 3.
Maximum gradient for stop and restart: 1 in 3.

TECHNICAL DATA

Power Unit
Type: B.M.C., 2·2 litre, gasoline (22 NA).
Displacement: 2,199 c.c. (134·2 cu. in.).
Gross B.H.P.: 70 at 4,000 r.p.m.
Nett torque: 114 lb. ft. at 1,500 r.p.m.
Ignition type: Coil, 12 volt.
Fuel System
Type: Mechanical lift pump.
Type of fuel: Gasoline.
Air cleaner: Oil bath.
Fuel capacity: 20 gallons (Imp.) (*90·86 litres*).
Engine Lubrication
System: Wet sump.
Engine Cooling
System: Pressurised.
Wheels
Rims: 5·50″E × 16″ W.D. divided type (F.V. 84930).
Tyres: 7·50″ × 16″ 6 PR C.C. tread.
Tyre pump: Manual.
Chains: Commercial.
Transmission
Clutch: 9″ (0·228 *metres*) dia. single dry plate.
Gearbox: 4-speed synchromesh and reverse.
Transfer box: 2-speed.
Transfer box ratios: 1 : 1 and 2·02 : 1.

Transmission—*continued*
Propeller shafts: Telescopic with Hookes joints.
Axles: Hypoid bevel (front and rear).
Ratios: Top 5·125 : 1, bottom 41·927 : 1.
Differentials: Two.
Brakes
Foot: Hydraulic, all wheels, drum type.
Hand: Mechanical, on rear wheels.
Steering
System: Ackermann.
Turning circle: 50′ max. (*15·25 metres*).
Suspension
Front: Semi-elliptic leaf springs.
Rear: Semi-elliptic leaf springs.
Shock absorbers: Front hydraulic, telescopic double acting. Rear hydraulic, lever type double acting.
Towing Attachments
Type: Front, provision only. Rear, rotating/lockable hook (F.V.332151).
Electrical Equipment
Generator: 12 volt d.c.
Batteries: 12 volt (lead/acid) 57 A.H.
Suppression: To F.V.R.D.E. Specification 2051, Schedule B, Appendix D1.

MANUFACTURERS

Chassis: ⎫ BRITISH MOTOR CORPORATION (AUSTIN OR MORRIS),
Body: ⎭ Longbridge, Birmingham.

ALTERNATIVE ROLES

Emergency wireless carrier (without battery charging facilities).
Emergency stretcher carrier.

Truck General Service F.F.R.
(Austin Gipsy $\frac{3}{4}$ ton 4 x 4)
(Project State—Under Development)

Description: This vehicle is based on the current commercial 'Gipsy Mk. 4' long wheelbase specification. Changes to the commercial specification have been made to render the vehicle more acceptable for Service use, especially in the radio carrying role, these include 24 volt 90 amp. rectified A.C. electrical system with provision for charging the wireless batteries, full suppression of electrical euqipment, built-in equipment for radio role including—wireless table, battery carrier, two 100 AH batteries, co-axial aerial leads, H.F. aerial brackets, two operators seats, etc. Other specification changes are as for the Truck General Service (Austin Gipsy $\frac{1}{4}$ ton 4 × 4) (Exhibit No. 18).

Height: 6' 5½" (*1·96 m.*).   Length: 13' 11¾" (*4·23 m.*).
Width: 5' 6½" (*1·69 m.*).   Wheelbase: 9' 3" (*2·82 m.*).
Track: Front 4' 8½" (*1·42 m.*).   Rear 4' 7⅛" (*1·4 m.*).
Weight: Laden 5,744 lb. (*2,610 kg.*).   Unladen (including radio fittings but no radio sets) 3,990 lb. (*1,810 kg.*).

PERFORMANCE DATA

Speed, average maximum:
Road 45 m.p.h. (*72·4 km./h.*).   C.C. 10 m.p.h. (*16·09 km./h.*).
Range of action at average maximum speed: 280 miles (*450 km.*).
Gross power weight ratio (b.h.p. per ton): 27·4.
Maximum tractive effort, low gear (lb. per ton): 1,600.
Maximum climbing ability: 1 in 3.
Maximum gradient for stop and restart: 1 in 3.

TECHNICAL DATA

Power Unit
Type: B.M.C., 2·2 litre, gasoline (22NA).
Displacement: 2,199 c.c. (134·2 cu. in.).
Gross b.h.p.: 70 at 4,000 r.p.m.
Nett torque: 114 lb. ft. at 1,500 r.p.m.
Ignition type: Coil, 10 volt with resistor.

Fuel System
Type: Mechanical lift pump.
Type of fuel: Gasoline.
Air cleaner: Oil bath.
Fuel capacity: 20 gallons (*90·86 litres*).

Engine Lubrication
System: Wet sump.

Engine Cooling
System: Pressurised.

Wheels
Rims: 5·50″E × 16″ WD divided type (F.V.84930).
Tyres: 7·50″ × 16″—6 PR (light truck) C.C. tread.
Tyre pump: Manual.
Chains: Commercial.

Transmission
Clutch: 9″ (*0·228 metres*) dia. single dry plate.
Gearbox: 4-speed and reverse (synchromesh on 2nd, 3rd and 4th gears).
Transfer box: 2-speed.
Transfer box ratios: 1 : 1 and 2·02 : 1.
Propeller shafts: Telescopic with

Transmission—*continued*
Hookes couplings.
Axles: Hypoid bevel (front and rear).
Ratios: top 5·125 : 1, bottom 41·927 : 1.
Differentials: Two.

Brakes
Foot: Hydraulic, all wheel, drum type.
Hand: Mechanical (rear wheel) drum type.

Steering
System: Ackermann.
Turning circle: 50′ max. (*15·25 m.*).

Suspension
Front: Semi-elliptic leaf springs.
Rear: Semi-elliptic leaf springs.
Shock absorbers: Front, hydraulic, telescopic, double acting. Rear, hydraulic, lever type, double acting.

Towing Attachments
Type: Front, provision only. Rear, rotating/lockable hook (F.V. 332151).

Electrical Equipment
Generator: 24 volt A.C. with inbuilt Silicon divide rectifiers (90 amp. output).
Batteries: Vehicle, lead/acid 12 volt × 2, 43 A.H. Equipment, lead/acid 12 volt × 2, 100 A.H. (Provision is made for a second pair of batteries when increased capacity is required).
Suppression: Full suppression (F.V.R.D.E. Specification 2051, Schedule A, Appendix D1).

MANUFACTURERS

Chassis: ⎫ BRITISH MOTOR CORPORATION (AUSTIN OR MORRIS),
Body: ⎭ Longbridge, Birmingham.

ALTERNATIVE ROLES

No official alternative roles but may be used for electronic installations requiring 24 volts power supply.

Truck Cargo (Rover ¾ ton for Power Trailers)

(Project State—Performance Assessment Trials)

Description: This is a private venture experimental model produced by the Rover Co. Ltd. It incorporates the following features:—

(a) Increased engine power.

(b) Power drive transfer for trailed loads, allowing optional choice of 6 × 6, 6 × 4 or 6 × 2 wheel drive.

(c) Large diameter section tyres.

(d) Improved approach and departure angles.

(e) Lightweight style body capable of being stripped to reduce weight, for airporting operations.

These features will be assessed for possible incorporation in the next generation of ¾ ton trucks.

Height: 6′ 8″ (*2·03 m.*).   Length: 14′ 3″ (*4·35 m.*).
Width: 6′ 0″ (*1·83 m.*).   Wheelbase: 9′ 2″ (*2·8 m.*).
Track: Front 4′ 11½″ (*1·49 m.*).   Rear 4′ 11½″ (*1·49 m.*).
Weight: Unladen 3,300 lb. (*1500 kg.*) stripped; 3,800 lb. (*1730 kg.*) complete.   Laden 6,500 lb. (*2960 kg.*).
Gross train weight: 11,000 lb. (*5,000 kg.*).

PERFORMANCE DATA

	Solo	*With Trailer*
Speed, average maximum:		
Road	50 m.p.h. (*85 km./ph.*)	40 m.p.h. (*64·3 km./ph.*)
C.C.	25 m.p.h. (*42·5 km./ph.*)	20 m.p.h. (*32·2 km./ph.*)
Range of action at average maximum speed:	300 miles (*482·5 km.*)	250 miles (*425 km.*)
Gross power weight ratio (b.h.p. per ton):	37·9	22·4
Maximum tractive effort, low gear (lb. per ton):	2850	1680
Maximum climbing ability:	1 in 1·6	1 in 2·7
Maximum gradient for stop and restart:	1 in 1·75	1 in 2·9

TECHNICAL DATA

Power Unit
Type: Rover, 3 L7, gasoline.
Displacement: 2,995 c.c. (182·7 cu. in.).
Gross B.H.P.: 110 at 4,500 r.p.m.
Nett torque: 152 lb. ft. at 1,500 r.p.m.
Ignition type: 12 volt coil.

Fuel System
Type: Dual electric pumps.
Type of fuel: Gasoline.
Air cleaner: Oil bath with pre-cleaner.
Fuel capacity: 20 gallons (*90·91 litres*).

Engine Lubrication
System: Wet sump.

Engine Cooling
System: Pressurised.

Wheels
Rims: 6½″ L × 16″ well base.
Tyres: 9·00″ × 16″ C.C.
Chains: Provision for fitting front and rear.

Transmission
Clutch: 10″ (*·253 metres*) S.D.P.
Gearbox: 4-speed synchromesh and reverse.
Transfer box: 2-speed.
Transfer box ratios: 0·975: 1 high, 3·27 : 1 low.
Propeller shafts: Hooke's type.
Axles: Spiral bevel, fully floating.
Ratios: Top: 5·432 : 1, bottom 72·506 : 1.

Transmission—*continued*
Differentials: Two.
Differential locks: Will be available.

Brakes
Foot: Hydraulic drum, with vacuum provision for trailer brakes.
Hand: Mechanical transmission.
Trailer: Single line inverted vacuum cylinder actuating hydraulic drum brakes.

Steering
System: Recirculating ball with articulated column.
Turning circle: R.H. 47′ (*14·35 metres*). L.H. 47′ (*14·35 metres*).

Suspension
Front: Semi-elliptic springs.
Rear: Semi-elliptic springs.
Shock absorbers: Front and rear hydraulic, telescopic, double acting.

Towing Attachments
Type: Front, standard hook. Rear, articulated coupling concentric with drive line to powered trailer, interchangeable with standard hook.

Electrical Equipment
Generator: 12 volt direct current or 24 volt 90 amp. alternator.
Batteries: One 12 volt 9 plate, or Two 12 volt 9 plate.
Suppression: To Schedule B or Schedule D requirement. F.V.R.D.E. Specification 2051, Appendix D1.

MANUFACTURERS

Chassis: ⎱ THE ROVER CO. LTD., Meteor Works,
Body: ⎰ Lode Lane, Solihull, Warwickshire.

Trailer Cargo Power Driven (1 ton)

(Project State—Engineering Model)

Description: This is a two-wheeled trailer which is capable of being towed with or without mechanical drive to the wheels. The chassis frame is steel welded construction with semi-elliptic suspension mounted on a differential axle. The tow eye and power driven coupling are interchangeable to suit the role. When the tow eye and hook are fitted the braking arrangement is by an over-run mechanism but if power driven coupling is fitted the brake operation is vacuum/mechanical. The power driven trailer role when coupled to a Landrover four wheel drive vehicle gives a six-wheel driven train with considerably higher mobility over soft terrain particularly if gradients are to be climbed.

Height: Chassis top 27″, body 49″.   Length: 9′ 11½″ (*3·04 m.*).

Width: 5′ 11″ (*1·80 m.*).   Track: 4′ 11½″ (*1·51 m.*).

Weight: Unladen 1,350 lb. (*611 kg.*) estimated.   Laden 3,590 lb. (1 ton payload) (*1,625 kg.*).

TECHNICAL DATA

Wheels
Rims: 650″L × 16″.
Tyres: 9·00″ × 16″, 6 ply light-
weight C.C. tread.

Transmission
Propeller shafts: Hardy Spicer.
Axle: Spiral bevel.

Brakes
Trailer: Mechanical hand brake
and service brakes.

Suspension
Semi-elliptic springs and Avon
rubber assistors.
Shock absorbers: Hydraulic, telescopic double acting.

MANUFACTURERS

Chassis:
Body: } Rubery, Owen & Co. Ltd., Darlaston, Staffs.

Truck Cargo Forward Control
(Rover 1 ton 4 x 4)
(Project State—Assessment Trials at F.V.R.D.E.)

Description: This vehicle is a commercial development based on the current 109″ wheelbase specification. The cab has been moved forward to a position over the front axle, has been raised to achieve the necessary clearance with the engine and front wheels. Heavy duty axles manufactured by E.N.V. have been fitted, these are of wider wheel track which together with wider spaced rear springs compensates for the higher centre of gravity of this vehicle which results from the provision of a flat platform type body. The vehicle exhibited is powered by a $2\frac{1}{4}$ litre engine which is common to the Landrover range, but alternative power units are available. The vehicle is undergoing assessment at F.V.R.D.E. as a 1 ton load carrier.

Height: (cab) 7′ $4\frac{1}{2}$″ (*2·25 m.*), (canopy) 8′ 6″ (*2·59 m.*).
Length: 16′ $7\frac{1}{2}$″ (*5·07 m.*).
Width: 5′ $10\frac{3}{4}$″ (*1·8 m.*).   Wheelbase: 9′ 2″ (*2·8 m.*).

Track: Front 4' 9½" (*1·46 m.*).   Rear: 4' 9½" (*1·46 m.*).
Weight: Unladen 4,480 lb. (*2,036 kg.*).   Laden 7,120 lb. (*3,240 kg.*).

PERFORMANCE DATA

Speed, average maximum:
    Road 40 m.p.h. (*64·3 km./h.*).
    C.C. 10 m.p.h. (*16·09 km./h.*).
Range of action at average maximum speed: 170 miles (*273 km.*).
Gross Power weight ratio (b.h.p. per ton): 24·2.
Maximum tractive effort, low gear (lb. per ton): 1,570.
Maximum climbing ability: 1 in 3.
Maximum gradient for stop and restart: 1 in 3.

TECHNICAL DATA

Power Unit
Type: Rover, 2¼ litre, gasoline.
Displacement: 2,286 c.c.
Gross B.H.P.: 77 at 4,250 r.p.m.
Nett torque: 116 lb. ft. at 1,500 r.p.m.
Ignition type: Coil, 12 volt.
Fuel System
Type: Mechanical lift-pump.
Type of Fuel: Gasoline.
Air cleaner: Oil bath with pre-cleaner.
Fuel capacity: 17 gallons (Imp.) (*77·2 litres*).
Engine Lubrication
System: Wet sump.
Engine Cooling
System: Pressurised.
Wheels
Rims: 6½L" × 16".
Tyres: 9·00" × 16" 6 ply C.C.
Tyre pump: Manual.
Chains: Commercial.
Transmission
Clutch: Enclosed S.D.P. 9½" (*0·24 m.*) dia.
Gearbox: 4-speed and reverse (synchromesh on 3rd and 4th gears).
Transfer box: 2-speed.
Transfer box ratios: 1·53 and 3·27: 1.

Propeller shafts: Telescopic with Hookes couplings.
Axles: Spiral bevel (front and rear).
Ratios: Top 7·19 : 1, bottom 55·4 : 1.
Differentials: Two.
Brakes
Foot: Hydraulic, all wheels, drum type.
Hand: Mechanical, transmission, drum type.
Steering
System: Ackermann.
Turning circle: 50' max. (*15·25 m.*).
Suspension
Front: Semi-elliptic leaf springs.
Rear: Semi-elliptic leaf springs.
Shock absorbers: Hydraulic, telescopic, double acting.
Towing Attachments
Type: Front, nil. Rear, rotating/lockable hook (FV. 332151).
Electrical Equipment
Generator: 12 volt D.C.
Batteries: 12 volt (lead/acid) 51 A.H. capacity.
Suppression: F.V.R.D.E.
Specification 2051, Schedule B, Appendix D1.

MANUFACTURERS

Chassis:⎫ THE ROVER CO. LTD., Meteor Works, Lode Lane, Solihull,
Body: ⎰ Warwickshire.

ALTERNATIVE ROLE

Possible Ambulance.

Truck Cargo (Austin 1½ ton 4 x 4)

(Project State—Under Development)

Description: This vehicle was designed to meet a requirement for a
G.S. 30 cwt. load carrier. It has a multi-fuel engine and all wheel drive.
Front wheel drive selection is controlled by the driver and is available
in all gear ratios. The vehicle shown is a prototype and is fitted with a
test body. In production, G.S. type cargo or specialist bodies could be
fitted. The load platform area is suitable for carrying the 1 ton container
at Exhibit No. 47.

Height: 7′ 5″ (*2·26 m.*).   Length: 15′ 11½″ (*4·87 m.*).
Width: 7′ 8″ (*2·335 m.*).   Wheelbase: 9′ 2″ (*2·79 m.*).
Track: Front 5′ 7″ (*1·7 m.*).   Rear 5′ 7″ (*1·7 m.*).
Weight: Unladen 6,888 lb. (*3,130 kg.*).   Laden 10,248 lb. (*4,660 kg.*).

PERFORMANCE DATA

Speed, average maximum:
    Road 40 m.p.h. (*64 km./h.*).
    C.C. 15 m.p.h.
Range of action at average maximum speed: 350 miles (*560 km.*).
Gross power weight ratio (b.h.p. per ton): 22·95.
Maximum tractive effort, low gear (lb. per ton): 2,500 lb./ton. (100% efficiency).
Maximum climbing ability: 1 in 1·5.
Maximum gradient for stop and restart: 1 in 2.

TECHNICAL DATA

Power Unit
Type: B.M.C., 5·7 litre, multi-fuel.
Displacement: 5,655 c.c. (345 cu. in.).
Gross b.h.p.: 105 at 2,400 r.p.m.
Nett torque: 248 lb. ft. at 1,450 r.p.m.
Governed speed: 2,400 r.p.m.
Ingition type: Compression.

Fuel System
Type: Pressurised, constant flow.
Type of fuel: Diesel or gasoline.
Air cleaner: Oil bath.
Fuel capacity: 20 gallons (*91 litres*).

Engine Lubrication
System: Wet sump.

Engine Cooling
System: Pressurised.

Wheels
Rims: B8·00″ × 16″.
Tyres: 11·00″ × 16″.
Tyre Pump: Optional.
Chains: Non-skid.

Transmission
Clutch: Single dry plate 13″ (*330 mm.*) dia.
Gearbox: 4-speed constant mesh.
Transfer box: 2-speed.

Transmission—*continued*
Transfer box ratios: 1·0 : 1 and 2·383 : 1.
Propeller shafts: Hardy Spicer.
Axles: Fully floating.
Ratios: top 4·88 : 1, bottom 70·5 : 1.
Differentials: Two.

Brakes
Foot: Air-hydraulic—dual air system.
Hand: Transmission, drum-manual.
Trailer: Air.
Warning device: Buzzer.

Steering
System: Cam gear.
Turning circle: R.H. 45′ (*13·7 metres*). L.H. 45′ (*13·7 metres*).

Suspension
Front: Semi-elliptic.
Rear: Semi-elliptic.
Shock absorbers: Armstrong lever type.

Towing Attachments
Type: Front, hook. Rear, hook.

Electrical Equipment
Generator: 12 or 24 volt.
Batteries: Two.
Suppression: Normal.

MANUFACTURERS

Chassis:⎫
Body: ⎬ AUSTIN MOTOR CO. LTD., Longbridge, Birmingham.

Truck Cargo (Rover 1½ ton 4 x 4)

(Project State—Under Development)

Description: This vehicle was designed to meet a requirement for a G.S. 30 cwt load carrier. It has a diesel engine and all wheel drive. Front wheel drive selection is controlled by the driver and is available in all gear ratios. The vehicle shown is a prototype and is fitted with a manufacturer's body. In production G.S. type cargo or specialist bodies could be fitted. The load platform area is suitable for carrying the 1 ton container at Exhibit No. 47.

Height: 8′ 8½″ (*2·66 m.*).   Length: 15′ 6½″ (*4·73 m.*).
Width: 7′ 3¼″ (*2·215 m.*).   Wheelbase: 9′ 4″ (*2·84 m.*).
Track: Front 5′ 6″ (*1·675 m.*).   Rear: 5′ 6″ (*1·675 m.*).
Weight: Unladen 7,460 lb. (*3,390 kg.*).   Laden: 10,850 lb. (*4,290 kg.*).

PERFORMANCE DATA

Speed, average maximum:
    Road 40 m.p.h. (*64 km./h.*).
    C.C. 15 m.p.h. (*24 km./h.*).
Range of action at average maximum speed: 420 miles (*673 km.*).
Gross power weight ratio (b.h.p. per ton): 21·7.
Maximum tractive effort, low gear (lb. per ton); 2,070.
Maximum climbing ability: 1 in 2.
Maximum gradient for stop and restart: 1 in 2.

TECHNICAL DATA

Power Unit.
6.354
Type: Perkins.
Displacement: 5,800 c.c. (354 cu. in.)
Gross B.H.P.: 105 at 2,500 r.p.m.
Nett torque: 243 lb. ft. at 1,450 r.p.m.
Governed speed: 2,500 r.p.m.
Ignition type: Compression
Fuel System
Type: Pressurised, constant flow.
Type of Fuel: Diesel.
Air cleaner: Oil bath.
Fuel capacity: 28 gallons (*127·5 litres*).
Engine Lubrication
System: Wet sump.
Engine Cooling
System: Pressurised.
Wheels
Rims: 6·50″ × 16″.
Tyres: 11·00″ × 16″.
Tyre pump: Inflator.
Chains: Non-skid.
Transmission
Clutch: Single dry plate.
Gearbox: 5-speed and reverse.
Transfer box: 2-speed.
Transfer box ratios: 1 : 1 and 2·105 : 1.

Propeller shafts: Hardy Spicer.
Axles: Spiral bevel.
Ratios: top 4·67 : 1, bottom 74·55 : 1.
Differentials: Two.
Differential locks: Positive lock.
Brakes
Foot: Air assisted hydraulic.
Hand: Mechanical rear wheels.
Trailer: Air system.
Warning device: Gauge.
Steering
System: Recirculating ball.
Turning circle: R.H. 47′ 5″ (*14·44 metres*). L.H. 45′ 1″ (*13·74 metres*).
Suspension
Front: Semi-elliptic springs.
Rear: Semi-elliptic springs.
Shock absorbers: Hydraulic telescopic, double acting, front and rear.
Towing Attachments
Type: Front, hook. Rear, hook.
Electrical Equipment
Generator: 90 amp. 24 volt A.C. (A.C. 90).
Batteries: 12 volt U.K. 6TN two in series.
Suppression: To F.V.R.D.E. Specification 2051, Appendix D1, Schedule B.

MANUFACTURERS

Chassis:
Body: } ROVER COMPANY LIMITED.

Truck Cargo (Bedford 1½ ton 4 x 4)

(Project State—Under Development)

Description: This vehicle was designed to meet a requierment for a G.S. 30 cwt load carrier. It has a multi-fuel engine and all wheel drive. Front wheel drive selection is controlled by the driver and is available in all gear ratios. The vehicle shown is a prototype and is fitted with a test body. In production, G.S. type cargo or specialist bodies could be fitted. The load platform area is suitable for carrying the 1 ton container at Exhibit No. 47.

Height: 7′ 4″ (*2·23 m.*).   Length: 17′ 0″ (*5·18 m.*).
Width: 6′ 8″ (*2·03 m.*).   Wheelbase: 10′ 0″ (*3·05 m.*).
Track: Front 5′ 6″ (*1·675 m.*).   Rear: 5′ 6″ (*1·675 m.*).
Weight: Unladen 7,440 lb. (*3,380 m.*). Laden: 10,800 lb. (*4,910 kg.*).

PERFORMANCE DATA

Speed, average maximum:
  Road 40 m.p.h. (*64 km./h.*).
  C.C. 15 m.p.h. (*24 km./h.*).
Range of action at average maximum speed: 380 miles (*608 km.*).
Gross power weight ratio (b.h.p. per ton): 21·1.
Maximum tractive effort, low gear (lb. per ton): 1,865.
Maximum climbing ability: 1 in 2.
Maximum gradient for stop and restart: 1 in 2.

TECHNICAL DATA

Power Unit
Type: Bedford, 330 cu. in., multi-fuel.
Displacement: 5,418 c.c. (330·6 cu. in.).
Gross B.H.P.: 102 at 2,800 r.p.m.
Nett torque: 222 lb. ft. at 1,600 r.p.m.
Governed speed: 2,800 r.p.m.
Ignition type: compression.

Fuel System
Type: Pressurised constant flow.
Type of fuel: Diesel or gasoline.
Air cleaner: Oil bath type.
Fuel capacity: 26 gallons (*118 litres*).

Engine Lubrication
System: Wet sump.

Engine Cooling
System: Pressurised.

Wheels
Rims: B8·0″ × 16″.
Tyres: 11·00″ × 16″.
Tyre pump: Inflator.
Chains: Non-skid.

Transmission
Clutch: 12″ dia. single dry plate (*305 mm.*).
Gearbox: 4-speed synchromesh and reverse.
Transfer box: 2-speed.
Transfer box ratios: 2 : 1 and 1 : 1.

Transmission—*continued*
Propeller shafts: Hardy Spicer.
Axles: Fully floating double reduction.
Ratios: top 4·672 : 1, bottom 60·8 : 1.
Differentials: Two.
Differential locks: Optional.

Brakes
Foot: Air pressure/dual hydraulic.
Hand: Mechanical on rear brake drums.
Warning device: Pressure gauge.

Steering
System: Worm and sector.
Turning circle: R.H. 45′ (*13·7 metres*). L.H. 45′ (*13·7 metres*).

Suspension
Front: Semi-elliptic springs.
Rear: Semi-elliptic springs.
Shock absorbers: Telescopic.

Towing Attachments
Type: Front, hook. Rear, hook.

Electrical Equipment
Generator: A.C. 5/25 alternator.
Batteries: Two UK-6-TN 12 volt.
Suppression: To F.V.R.D.E.
Specification 2051, Appendix L I, Schedule B.

MANUFACTURERS

Chassis:
Body: } VAUXHALL MOTORS LTD., Luton, Beds, England.

Truck Cargo (Commer 1½ ton 4 x 4)
(Project State—Under Development)

Description: This vehicle was designed to meet a requirement for a G.S. 30 cwt load carrier. It has a multi fuel engine and an all wheel drive. Front wheel drive selection is controlled by the driver and is available in all gear ratios. The vehicle shown is a prototype and is fitted with a test body. In production, G.S. type cargo or specialist bodies could be fitted. The load platform area is suitable for carrying the 1 ton container at Exhibit No. 47.

Height: 7′ 2¾″ (*2·2 m.*).   Length: 17′ 3⅞″ (*5·28 m.*).
Width: 8′ 0″ (*2·44 m.*).   Wheelbase: 10′ 2″ (*3·1 m.*).
Track: Front 5′ 6″ (*1·675 m.*).   Rear: 5′ 6″ (*1·675 m.*).
Weight: Unladen 8,568 lb. (*3,900 kg.*).   Laden: 11,928 lb. (*5·430 kg.*).

PERFORMANCE DATA
Speed: average maximum:
    Road 57 m.p.h. (*91·2 km./h.*).   C.C. 20 m.p.h. (*32 km./h.*).

Range of action at average maximum speed: 250 miles (*400 km.*).
Gross power weight ratio (b.h.p. per ton); 19·7.
Maximum tractive effort, low gear (lb. per ton); 1,910.
Maximum climbing ability: 1 in 1·50.
Maximum gradient for stop and restart: 1 in 3.

TECHNICAL DATA

Power Unit
Type: Perkins Q6.354 multi-fuel.
Displacement: 5,800 c.c. (354 cu. in.).
Gross B.H.P.: 105 at 2,500 r.p.m.
Nett torque: 243 lb. ft. at 1,450 r.p.m.
Governed speed: 2,500 r.p.m.
Ignition type: Compression.

Fuel System
Type: Pressurised, constant flow.
Type of fuel: Diesel or gasoline.
Air cleaner: Oil bath with pre-cleaner.
Fuel capacity: 20 gallons (*90·9 litres*).

Engine Lubrication
System: Wet sump.

Engine Cooling
System: Pressurised.

Wheels
Rims: B8·0″ × 16″ three-piece.
Tyres: 11·00″ × 16″ cross country.
Chains: Non-skid.

Transmission
Clutch: Single dry plate dia. 13″ (*330 mm.*).
Gearbox: Synchromesh 4 forward and reverse.
Transfer box: 2-speed.

Transfer box ratios: 1·0 : 1 and 2·0 : 1.
Propeller shafts: Hardy Spicer.
Axles: Fully floating.
Ratios: top 4·664 : 1, bottom 60·5 : 1.
Differentials: Two, spiral bevel.
Differential locks: Positive lock.

Brakes
Foot: Air-hydraulic, split hyraulic system.
Hand: Rear wheels only, mechanical.
Warning device: Gauge.

Steering
System: Cam and double roller.
Turning circle: R.H. 52′ (*15·83 metres*). L.H. 52′ (*15·83 metres*).

Suspension
Front: Semi-elliptic.
Rear: Semi-elliptic.
Shock absorbers: Telescopic.

Towing Attachments
Type: Front, hook. Rear, hook.

Electrical Equipment
Generator: C.A.V. N 55.
Batteries: Lucas 6 TN.
Suppression: To F.V.R.D.E. Specification 2051, Appendix DI, Schedule B.

MANUFACTURERS

Chassis: ⎫
Body: ⎭ COMMER CARS LTD.

Truck Tipper (Bedford 3 ton SWB 4 x 4)

(Project State—In Service)

Description: This vehicle is a 4-wheel drive adaptation of the Bedford 7 ton commercial chassis which has been modified to meet the User requirement for a 3–5 ton tipper vehicle. The body is of all steel construction with a capacity of approximately $4\frac{1}{2}$ cu. yds. (*3·45 cub. metres*). A $2\frac{1}{2}$ ton winch is fitted driven from a power take off on the transfer box and provision is made for rear and forward winching.

F.V. Specification Number: Chassis 9103.   Body/Equipment 9661.

Height: 9′ 11″ (*3·02 m.*).   Length: 18′ 3″ (*5·56 m.*).
Width: 7′ 4½″ (*2·25 m.*).   Wheelbase: 11′ 0″ (*3·35 m.*).
Track: Front 6′ 1″ (*1·85 m.*).   Rear 5′ 7¼″ (*1·714 m.*).
Weight: Unladen 11,004 lb. (*4,991 kg.*).   Laden 21,600 (*9,797·6 kg.*).

PERFORMANCE DATA

Speed, average maximum:
    Road: 35 m.p.h. (*56 km./h.*).
    C.C. 12-15 m.p.h. (*19–24 km./h.*).
Range of action at average maximum speed: 250 miles (*400 km.*).
Gross power weight ratio (b.h.p. per ton): 13·8.
Maximum tractive effort, low gear (lb. per ton): 1,405.
Maximum climbing ability: 1 in 3.
Maximum gradient for stop and restart: 1 in 3.

TECHNICAL DATA

Power Unit
Type: Bedford, 300 cu. in. gasoline.
Displacement: 4,927 c.c. (300 cu. in.).
Gross B.H.P.: 130 at 3,200 r.p.m.
Nett Torque: 222 lb. ft. at 1,200 r.p.m.
Governed speed: 3,200 r.p.m.
Ignition type: Coil, 12 volt.
Fuel System
Type: Lift pump.
Type of fuel: Gasoline.
Air cleaner: Oil bath.
Fuel capacity: 26 gallons (*118 litres*).
Engine Lubrication
System: Wet sump.
Engine Cooling
System: Pressurised.
Wheels
Rims: 3 piece disc.
Tyres: 9·00″ × 20″ C.C.
Tyre pump: Air Servo compressor.
Chains: Non-skid front and rear.
Transmission
Clutch: Single dry plate.
Gearbox: 4-speed synchromesh and reverse.
Transfer box: 2-speed.
Transfer box ratios: 1 : 1 and 2 : 1.
Propeller shafts: Hardy Spicer.

Axles: Fully floating.
Ratios: Top 6·8 : 1, bottom 96 : 1.
Differentials: Two.
Brakes
Foot: Hydraulic.
Hand: Mechanical on rear wheels only.
Trailer: Air pressure.
Warning device: Gauge.
Steering
System: Semi-irreversible worm and sector.
Turning circle: R.H. 52′ (*15·85 metres*). L.H. 52′ (*15·85 metres*).
Suspension
Front: Semi-elliptic.
Rear: Semi-elliptic with helper springs.
Shock absorbers: Double-acting telescopic, front and rear.
Towing Attachments
Type: Front, towing eyes. Rear, hook.
Electrical Equipment
Generator: 12 volt, 297 watts maximum.
Batteries: 12 volt 80 amp./h.
Suppression: To F.V.R.D.E. Specification 2051, Appendix D1, Schedule B.

MANUFACTURERS

Chassis: VAUXHALL MOTORS LTD., Luton, Beds.
Body: EDBRO LTD., Bolton, Lancs.

ALTERNATIVE ROLES

Truck.
Tractor.

Dental Clinic Truck Mounted
(Bedford 3 ton 4 x 4)

(Project State—Vehicles in Service)

Description: A purpose built body fully equipped as a Dental Surgery. The body is thermally insulated and air conditioned by 2 type 52 air conditioning units. A companion vehicle is available to provide dental laboratory facilities for three technicians.

F.V. Specification Number: Chassis 9103. Body 9680.

Height: 11′ 8″ (*3·56 m.*).   Length: 21′ 7″ (*7·37 m.*).
Width: 8′ 0″ (*2·44 m.*).   Wheelbase: 13′ 0″ (*3·962 m.*).
Track: Front 6′ 1″ (*1·854 m.*).   Rear: 6′ 1″ (*1·85 m.*).
Weight: Laden 14,000 lb. (*6,350 kg.*).

PERFORMANCE DATA

Speed, average maximum:
Road 35 m.p.h. (*56 km./h.*).
C.C. 12 m.p.h. (*19·24 km./h.*).
Range of action at average maximum speed: 250 miles (*400 km.*).
Gross power weight ratio (b.h.p. per ton): *20*.
Maximum tractive effort, low gear (lb. per ton): 1,632.

TECHNICAL DATA

Power Unit
Type: Bedford, 300 cu. in. gasoline.
Displacement: 4,927 c.c. (300 cu. in.).
Gross B.H.P.: 130 at 3,200 r.p.m.
Nett torque: 222 lb. ft. at 1,200 r.p.m.
Governed speed: 3,200 r.p.m.
Ignition type: Coil 12 volt.

Fuel System
Type: Lift pump.
Type of fuel: Gasoline.
Air cleaner: F.V. oil bath.
Fuel capacity: 26 gallons (*118 litres*).

Engine Lubrication
System: Wet sump.

Engine Cooling
System: Pressurised.

Wheels
Rims: 3 piece disc.
Tyres: 11·00″ × 20″ cross country.

Transmission
Clutch: Single dry plate.
Gearbox: 4-speed synchromesh, 1 reverse.

Transmission—*continued*
Transfer box: 2-speed.
Propeller shafts: Hardy Spicer.
Axles: Fully floating front and rear.
Ratios: top 6·8, bottom 96·1.
Differentials: Two.

Brakes
Foot: Hydraulic, servo assisted.
Hand: Mechanical on rear wheels only.

Steering
System: Semi-reversible worm and sector.
Turning circle: R.H. 60′ (*18·29 metres*). L.H. 60′ (*18·29 metres*).

Suspension
Front: Semi-elliptic
Rear: Semi-elliptic
Shock absorbers: Telescopic.

Electrical Equipment
Generator: 12 volt 500W.
Batteries: 12 volt 72 A/H.
Suppression: To F.V.R.D.E. Specification 2051, Appendix D1, Schedule B.

MANUFACTURERS

Chassis: VAUXHALL MOTORS LTD., Luton, Beds.
Body: T. HARRINGTON & SONS LTD., Sussex.

Automotive Repair Shop Truck Mounted
(Bedford 3 ton 4 x 4)
(Project State—In Service)

Description: The chassis is a standard 3 ton 4 × 4 and the body is a standard Service design permanently attached to the chassis. In the role shown the body has been equipped with machine and hand tools, benches, welding and compressed air plant to provide workshop repair facilities in the field. This type of body is also used for a variety of other installations.

F.V. Specification Number: Chassis 9103. Body 9668. Equipment 9671.

Height: 10′ 4″ (*3·14 m.*).   Length: 20′ 10″ (*6·35 m.*).
Width: 8′ 2″ (*2·48 m.*).   Wheelbase: 13′ 0″ (*3·96 m.*).
Track: Front 6′ 1″ (*1·85 m.*).   Rear 6′ 1″ (*1·85 m.*).
Weight: Laden 16,352 lb. (*7,417 kg.*).

PERFORMANCE DATA

Speed, average maximum:
    Road 35 m.p.h. (*56 km./h.*).
    C.C. 12 m.p.h. (*19·24 km./h.*).
Range of action at average maximum speed: 250 miles (*400 km.*).
Gross power weight ratio (b.h.p. per ton): 16·6.
Maximum tractive effort, low gear (lb. per ton): 1,632.

TECHNICAL DATA

Power Unit
Type: Bedford 300 cu. in. gasoline.
Displacement: 4,927 c.c. (300 cu. ins.).
Gross B.H.P.: 130 at 3,200 r.p.m.
Nett torque: 222 lb. ft. 1,200 r.p.m.
Governed speed: 3,200 r.p.m.
Ignition type: Coil 12 volt.
Fuel System
Type: Lift pump.
Type of Fuel: Gasoline.
Air cleaner: F.V. oil bath.
Fuel capacity: 26 gallons (*118 litres*).
Engine Lubrication
System: Wet sump.
Engine Cooling
System: Pressurised.
Wheels
Rims: 3 piece disc.
Tyres: 11·00″ × 20″ C.C.
Tyre pump: Air compressor.
Chains: Non-skid, all wheels.
Transmission
Clutch: Single dry plate.
Gearbox: 4-speed synchromesh 1 reverse.
Transfer box: 2-speed.
Transfer box ratios: 1 : 1 and 2 : 1.

Propeller shafts: Hardy Spicer.
Axles: Fully floating front and rear.
Ratios: Top 6·8 : 1, bottom 96·1 : 1.
Differentials: Two.
Brakes
Foot: Hydraulic air servo assisted.
Hand: Mechanical on rear wheels only.
Trailer: Air pressure.
Warning device: Gauge.
Steering
System: Semi-reversible worm and sector.
Turning circle: R.H. 60′ (*18·29 metres*). L.H. 60′ (*18·29 metres*).
Suspension
Front: Semi-elliptic.
Rear: Semi-elliptic.
Shock absorbers: Telescopic.
Towing Attachments
Type: Front, eyes. Rear, hook.
Electrical Equipment
Generator: 12 volt 297 watts.
Batteries: 12 volt 72 amp./h.
Suppression: To F.V.R.D.E. Specification 2051, Appendix D1, Schedule B.

MANUFACTURERS

Chassis: VAUXHALL MOTORS LTD., Luton, Beds.
Body: MARSHALL MOTOR BODIES LTD., Cambridge.

ALTERNATIVE ROLES

Signals installation.

Truck, Cargo Airportable Dropside
(Bedford 3 ton 4 x 4)
(Project State—In Service)

Description: This vehicle is a 4-wheeled drive adaptation of the Bedford 7-ton commercial chassis which has been modified to meet Service requirements for a 3 ton airportable vehicle. The top section of the cab is easily removable, the steering column can be lowered and a front spring compression device is fitted. With these three modifications the overall cab height can be reduced to 75″ (*1·92 m.*). The body is designed for the carriage of personnel in addition to general cargo. Body sides and tailboard are removable and the front bulkhead has a removable section to meet the requirement for the 75″ (*1·92 m.*) overall height.

F.V. Specification Number: Chassis 9103.   Body 9629.

Height: 10′ 0″ (*3·05 m.*).   Length: 20′ 10″ (*6·35 m.*).
Width: 7′ 9″ (*2·36 m.*).   Wheelbase: 13′ 0″ (*3·96 m.*).
Track: Front 6′ 1″ (*1·85 m.*).   Rear 6′ 1″ (*1·85 m.*).
Weight: Unladen 9,912 lb. (*4,496 kg.*).   Laden 18,000 lb. (*8,164 kg.*).

PERFORMANCE DATA

Speed, average maximum:
    Road 35 m.p.h. (*56 km./h.*).
    C.C. 12–15 m.p.h. (*19–24 km./h.*).
Range of action at average maximum speed: 250 miles (*400 km.*).
Gross power weight ratio (b.h.p. per ton): 16·6.
Maximum tractive effort, low gear (lb. per ton): 1,632.
Maximum climbing ability: 1 in 3.
Maximum gradient for stop and restart: 1 in 3.

TECHNICAL DATA

Power Unit
Type: Bedford, 300 cu. in. gasoline.
Displacement: 4,927 c.c. (300 cu. in.).
Gross: B.H.P.: 130 at 3,200 r.p.m.
Nett torque: 222 lb. ft. at 1,200 r.p.m.
Governed speed: 3,200 r.p.m.
Ignition type: Coil, 12 volt.
Fuel System
Type: Lift pump.
Type of fuel: Gasoline.
Air cleaner: Oil bath.
Fuel capacity: 26 gallons (*118 litres*).
Engine Lubrication
System: Wet sump.
Engine Cooling
System: Pressurised.
Wheels
Rims: 3 piece disc.
Tyres: 11·00″ × 20″ C.C.
Tyre pump: Air servo compressor.
Chains: Non-skid front and rear.
Transmission
Clutch: Single dry plate.
Gearbox: 4-speed synchromesh and reverse.
Transfer box: 2-speed.
Transfer box ratios: 1 : 1 and 2 : 1.
Propeller shafts: Hardy Spicer.

Axles: Fully floating.
Ratios: Top 6·8 : 1, bottom 96·1 : 1.
Differentials: Two.
Brakes
Foot: Hydraulic.
Hand: Mechanical on rear wheels only.
Trailer: Air pressure.
Warning device: Gauge.
Steering
System: Semi-irreversible worm and sector.
Turning circle: R.H. 60′ (*18·3 metres*). L.H. 60′ (*18·3 metres*).
Suspension
Front: Semi-elliptic.
Rear: Semi-elliptic.
Shock absorbers: Double-acting telescopic front and rear.
Towing Attachments
Type: Front: Towing eyes. Rear, hook.
Electrical Equipment
Generator: 12 volt, 297 watts maximum.
Batteries: 12 volt 80 amp./h.
Suppression: To F.V.R.D.E.
Specification 2051, Appendix D1, Schedule B.

MANUFACTURERS

Chassis: VAUXHALL MOTORS LTD., Luton, Beds.
Body: MARSHALL OF CAMBRIDGE (ENGINEERING) LTD., Cambridge.

ALTERNATIVE ROLES

Bulk fuel tanker.
Refueller.

Truck Cargo Dropside (Bedford 3 ton 4 x 4)

(Project State—In Service)

Description: This vehicle is a 4 wheel drive adaptation of the Bedford 7-ton commercial chassis which has been modified to meet Service requirements for a 3-ton vehicle.   The body is designed for the carriage of personnel in addition to general cargo. Body sides and tailboard can be dropped or removed.

F.V. Specification Number: Chassis 9103.   Body/Equipment 9629.

Height: 10′ 0″ (*3·05 m.*).   Length: 20′ 10″ (*6·35 m.*).
Width: 7′ 9″ (*2·36 m.*).   Wheelbase: 13′ 0″ (*3·96 m.*).
Track: Front 6′ 1″ (*1·85 m.*).   Rear 6′ 1″ (*1·85 m.*).
Weight: Unladen 9,912 lb. (*4,496 kg.*). Laden 18,000 lb. (*8,164 kg*).

PERFORMANCE DATA

Speed, average maximum:
    Road 35 m.p.h. (*56 km./h.*).
    C.C. 12–15 m.p.h. (*19-24 km./h.*).
Range of action at average maximum speed: 250 miles (*400 km.*).
Gross power weight ratio (b.h.p. per ton): 16·6.
Maximum tractive effort, low gear (lb. per ton): 1,632.
Maximum climbing ability: 1 in 3.
Maximum gradient for stop and restart: 1 in 3.

TECHNICAL DATA

Power Unit
Type: Bedford, 300 cu. in. gasoline.
Displacement: 4,927 c.c. (300 cu. in.).
Gross B.H.P.: 130 at 3,200 r.p.m.
Nett torque: 222 lb. ft. at 1,200 r.p.m.
Governed speed: 3,200 r.p.m.
Ignition type: Coil, 12 volt.
Fuel System
Type: Lift pump.
Type of fuel: Gasoline.
Air cleaner: Oil bath.
Fuel Capacity: 26 gallons (*118 litres*).
Engine Lubrication
System: Wet sump.
Engine Cooling
System: Pressurised.
Wheels
Rims: 3 piece disc.
Tyres: 11·00″ × 20″ C.C.
Tyre pump: Air servo compressor.
Chains: Non-skid front and rear.
Transmission
Clutch: Single dry plate.
Gearbox: 4-speed synchromesh and reverse.
Transfer box: 2-speed.
Transfer box ratios: 1 : 1 and 2 : 1.
Propeller shafts: Hardy Spicer.

Axles: Fully floating.
Ratios: Top 6·8 : 1, bottom 96·1 : 1.
Differentials: Two.
Brakes
Foot: Hydraulic.
Hand: Mechanical on rear wheels only.
Trailer: Air pressure.
Warning device: Gauge.
Steering
System: Semi-irreversible worm and sector.
Turning circle: R.H. 60′ (*18·3 metres*). L.H. 60′ (*18·3 metres*).
Suspension
Front: Semi-elliptic.
Rear: Semi-elliptic.
Shock absorbers: Double-acting telescopic front and rear.
Towing Attachments
Type: Front, towing eye. Rear, hook.
Electrical Equipment
Generator: 12 volt 297 watts maximum.
Batteries: 12 volt 80 amp./h.
Suppression: F.V.R.D.E.
Specification 2051, Appendix D1, Schedule B.

MANUFACTURERS

Chassis: VAUXHALL MOTORS LTD., Luton, Beds.
Body: MARSHALL OF CAMBRIDGE (ENGINEERING) LTD., Cambridge.

ALTERNATIVE ROLES

Bulk fuel tank.
Refueller.

Truck, Cargo (Bedford RK 4½ ton 4 x 4)

(Project State—Under Development)

Description: This vehicle has been designed to meet the general Service requirement for a 4½ ton vehicle. The payload of 4½ tons is for unrestricted use with an aluminium body and can be increased to 5 tons for road use only. The aluminium body exhibited is not representative of production design which will be about 5″ lower as for Exhibit Nos. 33 and 34. Chassis components are either identical to or based on units in production for commercial vehicles. The engine is a direct injection 6 cylinder 4 stroke operating on the diesel cycle and is suitable for multi-fuel operation.

Height: 11′ 0¾″ (*3·37 m.*).   Length: 21′ 10″ (*6·65 m.*).
Width: 8′ 0″ (*2·44 m.*).   Wheelbase: 13′ 0″ (*3·96 m.*).
Track: Front 6′ 8⅞″ (*2·05 m.*).   Rear: 6′ 8½″ (*2·045 m.*).
Weight: Unladen 10,752 lb. (*4,880 kg.*).   Laden: 20,832 lb. (*9,470 kg.*).

PERFORMANCE DATA

Speed, average maximum:
Road 35 m.p.h. (*56 km./h.*).   C.C. 12–15 m.p.h. (*19–24 km./h.*).
Range of action at average maximum speed: 360 miles (*576 km.*).
Gross power weight ratio (b.h.p. per ton): 10·95.
Maximum tractive effort, low gear (lb. per ton): 1,305.
Maximum climbing ability: In excess of 1 in 3.
Maximum gradient for stop and restart: 1 in 3.

TECHNICAL DATA

Power Unit
Type: Bedford, 330 cu. in. multi-fuel.
Displacement: 5,418 c.c. (330·6 cu. in.).
Gross: B.H.P.: 102 at 2,800 r.p.m.
Nett torque: 222 lb. ft. at 1,600 r.p.m.
Governed speed: 2,800 r.p.m.
Ignition type: Compression.

Fuel System
Type: Pressurised, constant flow.
Type of fuel: Diesel or gasoline.
Air cleaner: AC Delco, oil bath.
Fuel capacity: 26 gallons (*118 litres*).

Engine Lubrication
System: Wet sump.

Engine Cooling
System: Pressurised.

Wheels
Rims: 3-piece disc B 8·0 × 20.
Tyres: 12·00 × 20.
Tyre pump: Compressor.
Chains: Non-skid.

Transmission
Clutch: 13″ single dry plate (*512mm.*).
Gearbox: 4-speed synchromesh 1 reverse.
Transfer box: 2-speed.
Transfer box ratios: 2 : 1 and 1 : 1.

Transmission—*continued*
Propeller shafts: Hardy Spicer.
Axles: Fully floating.
Ratios: Top, 6·8 : 1, bottom 96·02 : 1.
Differentials: Two.

Brakes
Foot: Air/hydraulic.
Hand: Transmission, mechanical, drum.
Trailer: 2-line air pressure.
Warning device: Gauge.

Steering
System: Semi-irreversible worm and sector.
Turning circle: R.H. 58′ 8″ (*17·88 metres*). L.H. 58′ 7″ (*17·87 metres*).

Suspension
Front: Semi-elliptic leaf.
Rear: Semi-elliptic leaf.
Shock absorbers: Girling, telescopic, hydraulic.

Towing Attachments
Type: Front, hook. Rear, hook.

Electrical Equipment
Generator: 24 volt AC5/25.
Batteries: Two 12 volt UK-6-TN.
Suppression: To F.V.R.D.E. Specification 2051, Appendix D1, Schedule B.

MANUFACTURERS

Chassis: Vauxhall Motors Ltd., Luton, Beds.
Body: Marshall of Cambridge (Engineering) Ltd.

ALTERNATIVE ROLES

1. Bulk liquid.
2. Refueller.
3. Light recovery.
4. Container bodies (various), within load limits.

Truck Cargo
(Bedford RK 4½ ton 4 x 4 with Aluminium Body)

(Project State—Under Development)

Description: This vehicle has been designed to meet the General Service requirement for a 4½ ton vehicle. With the aluminium cargo body a payload of 4½ tons is permissible for unrestricted use and 5 tons for road use only. Chassis components are either identical to or based on production for commercial vehicles. The engine is a 6-cylinder direct injection 4 stroke operating on the diesel cycle and is suitable for multi-fuel operation.

Height: 11′ 0¼″ (*3·37 m.*).   Length: 21′ 10″ (*6·65 m.*).
Width: 8′ 0″ (*2·44 m.*).   Wheelbase: 13′ 0″ (*3·96 m.*).
Track: Front 6′ 8⅞″ (*2·05 m.*).   Rear 6′ 8½″ (*2·045 m.*).
Weight: Unladen 10,752 lb. (*4,880 kg.*). Laden: 20,832 lb. (*9,470 kg.*).

PERFORMANCE DATA

Speed, average maximum:
Road 35 m.p.h. (*56 km./h.*).
C.C. 12–15 m.p.h. (*19–24 km./h.*).
Range of action at average maximum speed: 360 miles (*576 km.*).
Gross power weight ratio (b.h.p. per ton): 10·95.
Maximum tractive effort, low gear (lb. per ton): 1,305.
Maximum climbing ability: 1 in 3.
Maximum gradient for stop and restart: 1 in 3.

TECHNICAL DATA

Power Unit
Type: Bedford, 330 cu. in. multi-fuel.
Displacement: 5,418 c.c. (330·6 cu. in.).
Gross B.H.P.: 102 at 2,800 r.p.m.
Nett torque: 222 lb. ft. at 1,600 r.p.m.
Governed speed: 2,800 r.p.m.
Ignition type: Compression.
Fuel System
Type: Pressurised, constant flow.
Type of fuel: Diesel or gasoline.
Air cleaner: A.C. Delco oil bath.
Fuel capacity: 26 gallons (*118 litres*).
Engine Lubrication
System: Wet sump.
Engine Cooling
System: Pressurised.
Wheels
Rims: 3 piece disc B 8·0″ × 20″.
Tyres: 12·00″ × 20″.
Tyre pump: Compressor.
Chains: Non-skid.
Transmission
Clutch: 13″ single dry plate (*512 mm.*).
Gearbox: 4-speed synchromesh and reverse.
Transfer box: 2-speed.

Transfer box ratios: 2 : 1 and 1 : 1.
Propeller shafts: Hardy Spicer.
Axles: Fully floating.
Ratios: Top 6·8 : 1, bottom 96·02 : 1.
Differentials: Two.
Brakes
Foot: Air-hydraulic.
Hand: Mechanical drum on transmission.
Trailer: 2-line air pressure.
Warning device: Gauge.
Steering
System: Semi-irreversible worm and sector.
Turning circle: R.H. 58′ 8″ (*17·88 metres*). L.H. 58′ 7″ (*17·87 metres*).
Suspension
Front: Semi-elliptic leaf.
Rear: Semi-elliptic leaf.
Shock absorbers: Girling, telescopic, hydraulic.
Towing Attachments
Type: Front, hook, Rear, hook.
Electrical Equipment
Generator: 24 volt a.c.5/25.
Batteries: Two, 12 volt U.K.-6-T.N.
Suppression: To F.V.R.D.E. Specification 2051, Appendix D1, Schedule B.

MANUFACTURERS

Chassis: VAUXHALL MOTORS LTD., Luton, Beds.
Body: MARSHALL OF CAMBRIDGE (ENGINEERING) LTD.

ALTERNATIVE ROLES

Light recovery.

Truck, Cargo with Winch
(Bedford RK 4½ ton 4 x 4 with Steel Body)
(Project State—Under Development)

Description: This vehicle is similar to F.V. 13801 (Exhibit No. 32) but is fitted with a steel body and a horizontal spindle winch. In this condition the payload is 3½ tons for unrestricted use, or 4 tons with an aluminium body. The winch has a maximum pull of 5 tons and uses 250′ of cable which can be deployed to the front and rear through a pay-on gear and fairleads. Brackets for wheel scotches are fitted.

Height: 11′ 0¾″ (*3·37 m.*).   Length: 21′ 10″ (*6·65 m.*).
Width: 8′ 0″ (*2·44 m.*).   Wheelbase: 13′ 0″ (*3·96 m.*).
Track: Front (6′ 8⅞″ (*2·05 m.*).   Rear: 6′ 8½″ (*2·045 m.*).
Weight: Unladen 12,992 lb. (*5,910 kg.*).   Laden: 20,832 lb. (*9,470 kg.*).

PERFORMANCE DATA

Speed, average maximum:
    Road 35 m.p.h. (*56 km./h.*).   C.C. 12–15 m.p.h. (*19-24 km./h.*).
Range of action at average maximum speed: 360 miles (*576 km.*).

Gross power weight ratio (b.h.p. per ton): 10·95.
Maximum tractive effort, low gear (lb. per ton): 1,305.
Maximum climbing ability: 1 in 3.
Maximum gradient for stop and restart: 1 in 3.

TECHNICAL DATA

Power Unit
Type: Bedford, 330 cu. in. multi-fuel.
Displacement: 5,418 c.c. (330·6 cu. in.).
Gross B.H.P.: 102 at 2,800 r.p.m.
Nett torque: 222 lb. ft. at 1,600 r.p.m.
Governed speed: 2,800 r.p.m.
Ignition type: Compression.
Fuel System
Type: Pressurised, constant flow.
Type of fuel: Diesel or gasoline.
Air cleaner: A.C. Delco oil bath.
Fuel capacity: 26 gallons (*118 litres*).
Engine Lubrication
System: Wet sump.
Engine Cooling
System: Pressurised.
Wheels
Rims: 3-piece disc B8·0″ × 20″.
Tyres: 12·00″ × 20″.
Tyre pump: Compressor.
Chains: Non-skid.
Transmission
Clutch: 13″ single dry plate (*512 mm.*).
Gearbox: 4-speed synchromesh and reverse.
Transfer box: 2 speed.
Transfer box ratios: 2 : 1 and 1 : 1.

Transmission—*continued*
Propeller shafts: Hardy Spicer.
Axles: Fully floating.
Ratios: Top 6·8 : 1, bottom 96·02 : 1.
Differentials: Two.
Brakes
Foot: Air-hydraulic.
Hand: Transmission, mechanical drum.
Trailer: 2 line air pressure.
Warning device: Gauge.
Steering
System: Semi-irreversible worm and sector.
Turning circle: R.H. 58′ 8″ (*17·88 metres*). L.H. 58′ 7″ (*17·87 metres*).
Suspension
Front: Semi-elliptic leaf.
Rear: Semi-elliptic leaf.
Shock absorbers: Girling, telescopic hydraulic.
Towing Attachments
Type: Front, hook. Rear, hook.
Electrical Equipment
Generator: 24 volt a.c.5/25.
Batteries: Two 12 volt U.K.-6-TN.
Suppression: To F.V.R.D.E. Specification 2051, Appendix D1, Schedule B.

MANUFACTURERS

Chassis: VAUXHALL MOTORS LTD., Luton, Beds.
Body: MARSHALL OF CAMBRIDGE (ENGINEERING) LTD.

ALTERNATIVE ROLES

1. Bulk liquid.
2. Refueller.
3. Light recovery.
4. Container bodies (various), within load limits.

Truck Cargo with Winch
(Bedford R.K. $4\frac{1}{2}$ ton 4 x 4)
(Project State—Under Development)

Description: This vehicle is similar to F.V. 13801 (Exhibit No. 32) but is fitted with a horizontal spindle winch having a maximum pull of 5 tons. The winch drum carries 250′ of cable which can be deployed to the front and rear through a pay-on gear and fairleads. Brackets for wheel scotches are fitted. Due to the additional weight of the winch and gear the useful payload is reduced to $3\frac{1}{2}$ tons with a steel body or 4 tons with an aluminium body.

Height: 11′ $0\frac{3}{4}''$ (*3·37 m.*).   Length: 21′ 10″ (*6·65 m.*).
Width: 8′ 0″ (*2·44 m.*).   Wheelbase: 13′ 0″ (*3·96 m.*).
Track: Front 6′ $8\frac{7}{8}''$ (*2·05 m.*).   Rear 6′ $8\frac{1}{2}''$ (*2·045 m.*).
Weight: Unladen 11,872 lb. (*5,390 kg.*). Laden 20,832 lb. (*9,470 kg.*).

PERFORMANCE DATA

Speed, average maximum:
    Road 35 m.p.h. (*56 km./h.*).
    C.C. 12–15 m.p.h. (*19–24 km./h.*).
Range of action at average maximum speed: 360 miles (*576 km.*).
Gross power weight ratio (b.h.p. per ton): 10·95.
Maximum tractive effort, low gear (lb. per ton): 1,305.
Maximum climbing ability: 1 in 3.
Maximum gradient for stop and restart: 1 in 3.

TECHNICAL DATA

Power Unit
Type: Bedford, 330 cu. in, multi-fuel.
Displacement: 5,418 c.c. (330·6 cu. in.).
Gross B.H.P.: 102 at 2,800 r.p.m.
Nett torque: 222 lb. ft. at 1,600 r.p.m.
Governed speed: 2,800 r.p.m.
Ignition type: Compression.
Fuel System
Type: Pressurised, constant flow.
Type of fuel: Diesel or gasoline.
Air cleaner: A.C. Delco oil bath.
Fuel capacity: 26 gallons (*118 litres*).
Engine Lubrication
System: Wet sump.
Engine Cooling
System: Pressurised.
Wheels
Rims: 3 piece disc B. 8·0 × 20.
Tyres: 12·00″ × 20″.
Tyre pump: Compressor.
Chains: Non-skid.
Transmission
Clutch: 13″ single dry plate (*512 mm.*).
Gearbox: 4-speed synchromesh 1 reverse.
Transfer box: 2-speed.
Transfer box ratios: 2 : 1 and 1 : 1.

Transmission—*continued*
Propeller shafts: Hardy Spicer.
Axles: Fully floating.
Ratios: top 6·8 : 1, bottom 96·02 : 1.
Differentials: Two.
Brakes
Foot: Air-hydraulic.
Hand: Mechanical, drum, transmission.
Trailer: 2-line air pressure.
Warning device: Gauge.
Steering
System: Semi-irreversible worm and sector.
Turning circle: R.H. 58′ 8″ (*17·88 metres*). L.H. 58′ 7″ (*17·87 metres*).
Suspension
Front: Semi-elliptic leaf.
Rear: Semi-elliptic leaf.
Shock absorbers: Girling, telescopic, hydraulic.
Towing Attachments
Type: Front, hook. Rear, hook.
Electrical Equipment
Generator: 24 volt A.C.5/25.
Batteries: Two 12 volt U.K.–6–TN.
Suppression: To F.V.R.D.E.
Specification 2051, Appendix D1, Schedule B.

MANUFACTURERS

Chassis: VAUXHALL MOTORS LTD., Luton, Beds.
Body: MARSHALL OF CAMBRIDGE (ENGINEERING) LTD.

ALTERNATIVE ROLES

Light recovery.
Container bodies (various) within load limits.

Truck Cargo (Austin F.J. 4½ ton 4 x 4)
(Project State—Under Development)

Description: This vehicle has been designed to meet the general Service requirement for a 4½ ton vehicle. The payload of 4½ tons is for unrestricted use with an aluminium body and can be increased to 5 tons for road use only. The aluminium body exhibited is not representative of production design which would be about 5″ lower as for Exhibit Nos. 33 and 34. Chassis components are either identical to or based on units in production for commercial vehicles. The engine is a direct injection 6-cyl 4-stroke operating on the diesel cycle and is suitable for multifuel operation.

Height: 11′ 6⅜ (*3·52 m.*).
Length: 20′ 2¾″ (*6·17 m.*).
Width: 8′ 0″ (*2·44 m.*).
Wheelbase: 11′ 9″ (*3·581 m.*).
Track: Front 6′ 8⅝″ (*2·045 m.*).   Rear 6′ 8⅛″ (*2·03 m.*).
Weight: Unladen 12,740 lb. (*5,790 kg.*).   Laden 22,820 lb. (*10,390kg.*).

PERFORMANCE DATA

Speed, average maximum:
Road 37 m.p.h. (*59·2 km./hr.*).   C.C. 15 m.p.h. (*24 km./hr.*).
Range of action at average maximum speed: 390 miles (*624 km.*).
Gross power weight ratio (b.h.p. per ton): 9·8.
Maximum tractive effort, Low gear (lb. per ton): 1,540.
Maximum climbing ability: 1 in 3.
Maximum gradient for stop and restart: 1 in 3.

TECHNICAL DATA

Power Unit
Type: B.M.C., 5·7 litre, multi-fuel.
Displacement: 5,655 c.c. (345 cu. in.).
Gross B.H.P.: 105 at 2,400 r.p.m.
Nett torque: 248 lb. ft. at 1,450 r.p.m.
Governed speed: 2,400.
Ignition Type: Compression.

Fuel System
Type: Pressurised, constant flow.
Type of fuel: Diesel or gasoline.
Air Cleaner: AC Delco oil bath.
Fuel Capacity: 30 gallons (*136 litres*).

Engine Lubrication
System: Wet sump.

Engine Cooling
System: Pressurised.

Wheels
Rims: 3 piece disc B8·0 × 20.
Tyres: 12·00 × 20 C.C.
Tyre pump: Compressor.
Chains: Non skid.

Transmission
Clutch: 13″ dia. (*330 mm.*) single dry plate.
Gearbox: 5-speed and reverse (synchromesh).
Transfer box: 2-speed.
Transfer box ratios: 1 : 1 and 2·383 : 1.

Transmission—*continued*
Propeller shafts: Hardy Spicer.
Axles: Fully floating.
Ratios: top 6·67 : 1, bottom 110·2 : 1
Differentials: Two.

Brakes
Foot: Dual—air/hydraulic.
Hand: Mechanical disc on transmission.
Trailer: 2 line air pressure.
Warning device: Gauge and buzzer.

Steering
System: Cam gear high efficiency.
Turning circle: R.H. 60′ (*18·3 metres*). L.H. 60′ (*18·3 metres*).

Suspension
Front: Semi-elliptic.
Rear: Semi-elliptic.
Shock absorbers: Armstrong lever type.

Towing Attachments
Type Front, hook. Rear, hook.

Electrical Equipment
Generator: 24 volt AC5/25.
Batteries: Two UK-6-TN.
Suppression: To F.V.R.D.E.
Specification 2051, Appendix D1, Schedule B.

MANUFACTURERS

Chassis: AUSTIN MOTOR COMPANY LTD., Birmingham.
Body: MARSHALLS OF CAMBRIDGE (ENGINEERING) LTD.

ALTERNATIVE ROLES

1. Bulk liquid carrier.
2. Refueller.
3. Light recovery.
4. Container bodies (various) within load limits.

Truck Cargo with Winch
(Austin F.J. 4½ ton 4 x 4)
(Project State—Under Development)

Description: This vehicle is similar to F.V. 13701 (Exhibit No. 36 but is fitted with a horizontal spindle winch having a maximum pull of 5 tons. The winch drum carries 250′ of cable which can be deployed to the front or rear through a pay-on gear and fairleads. Brackets for wheel scotches are fitted. Due to the additional weight of the winch and gear the useful pay-load is reduced to 3½ tons with a steel body or 4 tons with an aluminium body.

Height: 11′ 6⅜″ (*3·52 m.*).
Length: 20′ 2¾″ (*6·17 m.*).
Width: 8′ 0″ (*2·44 m.*).
Wheelbase: 11′ 9″ (*3·581 m.*).
Track: Front 6′ 8⅝″ (*2·045 m.*).   Rear 6′ 8¼″ (*2·03 m.*).
Weight: Unladen 13,940 lb. (*6,340 kg.*).   Laden 22,820 lb. (*10,390 kg*).

PERFORMANCE DATA

Speed, average maximum:
> Road 37 m.p.h. (*59·2 km./h.*).
> C.C. 15 m.p.h. (*24 km/h.*).

Range of action at average maximum speed: 390 miles (*624 km.*).
Gross power weight ratio (b.h.p. per ton): 9·8.
Maximum tractive effort, low gear (lb. per ton): 1,540.
Maximum climbing ability: 1 in 3.
Maximum gradient for stop and restart: 1 in 3.

TECHNICAL DATA

Power Unit
Type: B.M.C., 5·7 litre, multi-fuel.
Displacement: 5,655 c.c. (345 cu. in.).
Gross B.H.P.: 105 at 2,400 r.p.m.
Nett torque: 248 lb. ft. at 1,450 r.p.m.
Governed speed: 2,400.
Ignition type: Compression.
Fuel System
Type: Pressurised constant flow.
Type of fuel: Diesel or gasoline.
Air cleaner: AC Delco oil bath.
Fuel capacity: 30 gallons (*136 litres*).
Engine Lubrication
System: Wet sump.
Engine Cooling
System: Pressurised.
Wheels
Rims: 3 piece disc. B8·0 × 20.
Tyres: 12·00 × 20 C.C.
Tyre pump: Compressor.
Chains: Non skid.
Transmission
Clutch: Single dry plate 13″ dia. (*330 mm.*).
Gearbox: 5-speed synchromesh 1 reverse.
Transfer box: 2-speed.
Transfer box ratios: 1 : 1 and 2·383 : 1.

Transmission—*continued*
Propeller shafts: Hardy Spicer.
Axles: Fully floating.
Ratios: Top 6·67 : 1, bottom 110·2 : 1.
Differentials: Two.
Brakes
Foot: Dual—air/hydraulic.
Hand: Mechanical disc on transmission.
Trailer: 2 line air pressure.
Warning device: Gauge and buzzer.
Steering
System: Cam gear high efficiency.
Turning circle: R.H. 60′ (*18·3 metres*). L.H. 60′ (*18·3 metres*).
Suspension
Front: Semi-elliptic leaf.
Rear: Semi-elliptic leaf.
Shock absorbers: Armstrong lever type.
Towing Attachments
Type: Front, hook. Rear, hook.
Electrical Equipment
Generator: 24 volt AC5/25.
Batteries: Two UK-6-TN.
Suppression: To F.V.R.D.E.
Specification 2051, Appendix D1, Schedule B.

MANUFACTURERS

Chassis: Austin Motor Co. Ltd., Birmingham.
Body: Marshall of Cambridge (Engineering) Ltd.

ALTERNATIVE ROLES

1. Light recovery.
2. Container bodies (various) within load limits.

Truck, Cargo (Commer CB $4\frac{1}{2}$ ton 4 x 4)

(Project State—Under Development)

Description: This vehicle has been designed to meet the general Service requirement for a $4\frac{1}{2}$ ton vehicle. The payload of $4\frac{1}{2}$ tons is for unrestricted use with an aluminium body and can be increased to 5 tons for road use only. The aluminium body exhibited is not representative of production design which will be about 5″ lower as for Exhibit Nos. 33 and 34. Chassis components are either identical to or based on units in production for commercial vehicles. The engine is a high speed direct injection scavenge blown two stroke with opposed pistons, operating on the diesel cycle and is suitable for multi-fuel operation.

Height: 11′ $3\frac{1}{2}$″ (*3·44 m.*).   Length: 21′ $1\frac{1}{2}$″ (*6·43 m.*).
Width: 7′ $11\frac{3}{4}$″ (*2·43 m.*).   Wheelbase: 13′ 6″ (*4·11 m.*).
Track: Front 6′ 8″ (*2·03 m.*).   Rear: 6′ $10\frac{3}{4}$″ (*2·1 m.*).
Weight: Unladen 11,872 lb. (*5,390 kg.*).   Laden: 21,952 lb. (*9,980 kg.*).

PERFORMANCE DATA

Speed, average maximum:
Road 37 m.p.h. (*59·2 km./h.*).   C.C. 15 m.p.h. (*24 km./h.*).
Range of action at average maximum speed: 350 miles (*560 km.*).
Gross Power weight ratio (b.h.p. per ton): 11·94.
Maximum tractive effort, low gear (lb. per ton): 1,220.
Maximum climbing ability: In excess of 1 in 3.
Maximum gradient for stop and restart: 1 in 3.

TECHNICAL DATA

Power Unit
Type: Rootes, TS.3A, multi-fuel, 2-stroke.
Displacement: 3.261 c.c. (199 cu. in.).
Gross B.H.P.: 117 at 2,400 r.p.m.
Nett torque: 298 lb. ft. at 1,250 r.p.m.
Governed speed: 2,400 r.p.m.
Ignition type: Compression.
Fuel System
Type: Pressurised, constant flow.
Type of fuel: Diesel or gasoline.
Air cleaner: Oil bath.
Fuel capacity: 30 gallons (*136 litres*).
Engine Lubrication
System: Wet sump.
Engine Cooling
System: Pressurised.
Wheels
Rims: 3-piece disc B 8·0 × 20.
Tyres: 12·00 × 20 C.C.
Tyre pump: Compressor.
Chains: Non-skid.
Transmission
Clutch: Single dry plate 14″ dia. (*355 mm.*).
Gearbox: 5-speed synchromesh 1 reverse.
Transfer box: 2-speed.
Transfer box ratios: 1·6 : 1 and 1 : 1.

Transmission—*continued*
Propeller shafts: Hardy Spicer.
Axles: Fully floating.
Ratios: Top, 5·875 : 1, bottom 70·4 : 1.
Differentials: Two.
Brakes
Foot: Air/hydraulic.
Hand: Transmission, mechanical, disc.
Trailer: 2-line air pressure.
Warning device: Gauge.
Steering
System: Cam and peg.
Turning circle: R.H. 64′ 2″ (*19·6 metres*). L.H. 61′ 7½″ (*19·4 metres*).
Suspension
Front: Semi-elliptic leaf.
Rear: Semi-elliptic leaf.
Shock absorbers: Armstrong, telescopic hydraulic.
Towing Attachments
Type: Front, hook. Rear, hook.
Electrical Equipment
Generator: 24 volt AC5/25.
Batteries: Two UK-6-TN.
Suppression: To F.V.R.D.E. Specification 2051, Appendix D1, Schedule B.

MANUFACTURERS

Chassis: COMMER CARS LTD., Luton, Beds.
Body: MARSHALL OF CAMBRIDGE (ENGINEERING) LTD., Motor Bodies Division, Airport Works, Cambridge.

ALTERNATIVE ROLES

1. Bulk liquid.
2. Refueller.
3. Light recovery.
4. Container bodies (various), within load limits.

Truck Cargo with Winch
(Commer CB $4\frac{1}{2}$ ton 4 x 4)

(Project State—Under Development)

Description: This vehicle is similar to F.V. 13901 (Exhibit No. 38) but is fitted with a horizontal spindle winch having a maximum pull of 5 tons. The winch drum carries 250′ of cable which can be deployed to the front and rear through a pay-on gear and fairleads. Brackets for wheel scotches are fitted. Due to the additional weight of the winch and gear the useful payload is reduced to $3\frac{1}{2}$ tons with a steel body or 4 tons with an aluminium body.

Height: 11′ $3\frac{1}{2}$″ (*3·44 m.*).   Length: 21′ $1\frac{1}{2}$″ (*6·43 m.*).
Width: 7′ $11\frac{3}{4}$″ (*2·43 m.*).   Wheelbase: 13′ 6″ (*4·11 m.*).
Track: Front 6′ 8″ (*2·03 m.*).   Rear: 6′ $10\frac{3}{4}$″ (*2·1 m.*).
Weight: Unladen 12,992 lb. (*5,910 kg.*).   Laden: 21,952 lb. (*9,980 kg.*).

PERFORMANCE DATA

Speed, average maximum:
  Road 37 m.p.h. (*59·2 km./h.*).
  C.C. 15 m.p.h. (*24 km./h.*).
Range of action at average maximum speed: 350 miles (*560 km.*).
Gross power weight ratio (b.h.p. per ton): 11·95.
Maximum tractive effort, low gear (lb. per ton): 1,220.
Maximum climbing ability: 1 in 3.
Maximum gradient for stop and restart: 1 in 3.

TECHNICAL DATA

Power Unit
Type: Rootes, TS.3A, multi-fuel, 2-stroke.
Displacement: 3,261 c.c. (199 cu. in.)
Gross B.H.P.: 117 at 2,400 r.p.m.
Nett torque: 298 lb. ft. at 1,250 r.p.m.
Governed Speed: 2,400 r.p.m.
Ignition type: Compression.

Fuel System
Type: Pressurised, constant flow.
Type of fuel: Diesel or gasoline.
Air cleaner: Oil bath.
Fuel capacity: 30 gallons (*136 litres*).

Engine Lubrication
System: Wet sump.

Engine Cooling
System: Pressurised.

Wheels
Rims: 3-piece disc B 8·0 × 20.
Tyres: 12·00 × 20 C.C.
Tyre pump: Compressor.
Chains: Non-skid.

Transmission
Clutch: Single dry plate 14″ dia. (355 *mm.*)
Gearbox: 5-speed synchromesh 1 reverse.
Transfer box: 2-speed.

Transmission—*continued*
Transfer box ratios: 1·6 : 1 and 1 : 1.
Propeller shafts: Hardy Spicer.
Axles: Fully floating.
Ratios: Top 5·875 : 1, bottom 70·4 : 1.
Differentials: Two.

Brakes
Foot: Air/hydraulic.
Hand: Transmission, mechanical disc.
Trailer: 2-line air pressure.
Warning device: Gauge.

Steering
System: Cam and peg.
Turning circle: R.H. 64′ 2″ (*19·6 metres*). L.H. 61′ 7½″ (*19·4 metres*).

Suspension
Front: Semi-elliptic leaf.
Rear: Semi-elliptic leaf.
Shock absorbers: Armstrong, telescopic hydraulic.

Towing Attachments
Type: Front, hook. Rear, hook.

Electrical Equipment
Generator: 24 volt AC5/25.
Batteries: Two UK-6-TN.
Suppression: To F.V.R.D.E. Specification 2051, Appendix D1, Schedule B.

MANUFACTURERS

Chassis: COMMER CARS LTD., Luton, Beds.
Body: MARSHALL OF CAMBRIDGE (ENGINEERING), LTD.

ALTERNATIVE ROLES

1. Light recovery.
2. Container bodies (various), within load limits.

Recovery Vehicle Wheeled-Light
(Bedford 3 ton 4 x 4)
(Project State—In Service)

Description: This vehicle is a standard 3 ton 4 × 4 G.S. (Bedford) chassis adapted for use as a recovery vehicle. The equipment is designed for the recovery of all wheeled vehicles up to and including the 3 ton G.S. class. The jib has a maximum safe working load of 3 tons at 8 ft. radius, the hoist winch drive being taken from a power take-off on the main gearbox. The main winch is driven from a power take off on the transfer gearbox and has a maximum first layer pull of 7 tons. Provision is made for both front and rear winching. With the assistance of a special sprag type earth anchor and two part tackle the winch can exert a maximum rear pull of 13 tons or side pull of 6 tons. The suspended tow hook capacity is 3 tons.

F.V. Specification Number: Chassis 9103. Body/Equipment 9223.

Height: 8′ 10½″ (*2·71 m.*).   Length: 26′ 2″ (*7·98 m.*).
Width: 7′ 7½″ (*2·32 m.*).   Wheelbase: 13′ 0″ (*3·96 m.*).
Track: Front 6′ 1″ (*1·86 m.*).   Rear 5′ 7¼″ (*1·71 m.*).
Weight: Laden 17,920 lb. (*8,128 kg.*).

PERFORMANCE DATA

Speed, average maximum:
    Road: 35 m.p.h. (*56 km./h.*).
    C.C. 12–15 m.p.h. (*19–24 km./h.*).
Range of action at average maximum speed: 250 miles (*400 km.*).
Gross power weight ratio (b.h.p. per ton): 16·63.
Maximum tractive effort, low gear (lb. per ton): 1,685.
Maximum climbing ability: 1 in 3.
Maximum gradient for stop and restart: (solo) 1 in 3.

TECHNICAL DATA

Power Unit
Type: Bedford, 300 cu. in. gasoline.
Displacement: 4,927 c.c. (300 cu. in.).
Gross B.H.P.: 130 at 3,200 r.p.m.
Nett torque: 222 lb. ft. at 1,200 r.p.m.
Governed speed: 3,200 r.p.m.
Ignition type: Coil, 12 volts.

Fuel System
Type: Lift pump.
Type of fuel: Gasoline.
Air cleaner: F.V. oil bath.
Fuel capacity: 26 gallons (*118 litres*).

Engine Lubrication
System: Wet sump.

Engine Cooling
System: Pressurised.

Wheels
Rims: 3-piece disc.
Tyres: 9·00″ × 20″ C.C.
Tyre Pump: Air servo compressor.
Chains: W.D. non-skid, all wheels.

Transmission
Clutch: Single dry plate.
Gearbox: 4-speed synchromesh and reverse.
Transfer box: 2-speed.
Transfer box ratios: 2 : 1 and 1 : 1.

Transmission—*continued*
Propeller shafts: Hardy Spicer.
Axles: Fully floating.
Ratios: Top 6·8 : 1, bottom 96 : 1.
Differentials: Two.

Brakes
Foot: Air/hydraulic, drum pattern all wheels.
Hand: Mechanical, rear only.
Trailer: 2 line air.
Warning device: Gauge.

Steering
System: Worm and sector.
Turning circle: R.H. 60′ (*18·29 metres*). L.H. 60′ (*18·29 metres*).

Suspension
Front: Semi-elliptic.
Rear: Semi-elliptic.
Shock absorbers: Double acting telescopic front and rear.

Towing Attachments
Type: Front, hook. Rear, hook.

Electrical Equipment
Generator: 12 volt 297 watts.
Batteries: 12 volt 80 amp./h.
Suppression: F.V.R.D.E. Specification 2051, Appendix D1, Schedule B.

MANUFACTURERS

Chassis: Vauxhall Motors Ltd., Luton Beds.
Body: Marshall of Cambridge (Engineering) Ltd., Cambridge.

Recovery Vehicle Wheeled Medium
(AEC Mk. 2, 10 ton 6 x 6)
(Project State—Undergoing development trials)

Description: This vehicle is the replacement for the existing in service Scammell 6 × 6 Recovery Tractor. It is capable of recovering on suspended tow all wheeled vehicles up to and including the 10 ton class. The hydraulic power operated crane has the following features: angle of slew 240°: jib length extensible from 10′ to 18′: jib luffing from horizontal to 48° up: lift and slew 1·5 ton at 18′ radius without outrigger jacks, 2·6 ton at 18′ radius with outrigger jacks: maximum hook height 22′: maximum lift on hoist cable 10′. The mechanically driven winch is rated at 12·3 ton continuous line pull for the full effective length of the winch rope and 15 ton pull on the bottom layer of the drum. A hydraulically operated spade is incorporated at the rear of the vehicle and when in use winch pulls up to 30 ton can be exerted.

F.V. Specification Number: Chassis 9337. Body 9707. Equipment 9707.

Height: 10' 4" (3·15 m.). Length: 25' 0" (7·62 m.).
Width: 8' 2½" (2·50 m.). Wheelbase: 12' 10½" (3·92 m.).
Track: Front 6' 6¾" (2·17 m.). Rear: 6' 9" (2·06 m.).
Weight: Solo 40,320 lb. (18,289 kg.).

PERFORMANCE DATA

Speed, average maximum:
    Road 34 m.p.h. (54·70 km./h.). C.C. 15 m.p.h. (24·13 km./h.).
Range of action at average maximum speed (solo): 350 miles (563 km.).
Gross power weight ratio (b.h.p. per ton) (solo): 12·6.
Maximum tractive effort, low gear (lb. per ton) (solo): 1,567.
Maximum gradient for stop and restart (solo): 1 in 3.

TECHNICAL DATA

Power Unit
Type: A.E.C., A.V.760., Diesel.
Displacement: 12,473 c.c. (761 cu. in.).
Gross B.H.P.: 226 at 2,200 r.p.m.
Nett torque: 555 lb. ft. at 1,500 r.p.m.
Governed speed: 2,200 r.p.m.
Ignition type: Compression.
Fuel System
Type: Lift pump.
Type of Fuel: Diesel.
Air Cleaner: Burgess oil bath.
Fuel capacity: 48 gallons (218 litres).
Engine Lubrication
System: Wet sump.
Engine Cooling
System: Pressurised.
Wheels
Rims: 4 piece disc type.
Tyres: 16·00" × 20" C.C.
Tyre Pump: Inflator from air compressor.
Chains: Non-skid front. Overall tracks rear.
Transmission
Clutch: Single dry plate.
Gearbox: 6-speed and reverse.
Transfer box: 2-speed.
Transfer box ratios: 1 : 1 and 1·87 : 1 reduction.
Propeller shafts: Hardy-Spicer.

Axles: Driven front and rear.
Ratios: top 5·925 : 1, bottom 105·92 : 1.
Differentials: Four.
Differential locks: Inter-axle and cross-axle locks.
Brakes
Foot: Air pressure on all wheels.
Hand: Mechanical, air assistance, rear wheels only.
Trailer: 3-line air pressure.
Warning device: Pressure gauge.
Steering
System: Worm and nut type. Hydraulic power assistance.
Turning circle: R.H. 66' dia. (20·12 metres). L.H. 66' dia. (20·12 metres).
Suspension
Front: Semi-elliptic.
Rear: Semi-elliptic.
Shock absorbers: Hydraulic type front only.
Towing Attachments
Type: Front, hook. Rear, hook.
Electrical Equipment
Generator: 28 volt 90 amp.
Batteries: 24 volt 100 amp./h.
Suppression: F.V.R.D.E. Specification 2051, Appendix D1, Schedule A.

MANUFACTURERS

Chassis: A.E.C. LTD., Southall, Middlesex.
Recovery
Equipment: SCAMMELL LORRIES LTD., Watford, Herts.
Crane: BRITISH CRANE AND EXCAVATOR CORPORATION LTD., Grantham, Lincs.

Recovery Vehicle Wheeled-Heavy
(Leyland 10 ton 6 x 6)

(Project State—In Service)

Description: This tractor is capable of recovering on suspended tow all wheeled vehicles up to and including the 10 ton class. The hydraulic power operated crane has the following features: Angle of slew 240: jib length extensible from 10′ to 18′: jib luffing from horizontal to 45° up: load capacity 15 ton with jib stays to ground: 1·5 ton at maximum radius without stays: maximum hook height 20′: maximum lift 27′. A hydraulic winch is fitted incorporating two speed ranges which give the following alternative maximum rope pulls and speeds: low range 15 ton at 15′/min.: high range 5 ton at 45′/min. A hydraulically operated spade is provided at the rear of the vehicle and when in use, rear pulls of up to 40 ton can be exerted.

F.V. Specification Number: Chassis 9171. Body 9083.

Height: 10′ 2″ (*3·10 m.*).   Length: 29′ 2″ (*8·89 m.*).
Width: 8′ 6″ (*2·59 m.*).   Wheelbase: 14′ 6″ (*4·42 m.*).
Track: Front 6′ 10½ ″ (*2·10 m.*).   Rear 6′ 10½″ (*2·10 m.*).
Weight: Solo 47,628 lb. (*21,604 kg.*).

PERFORMANCE DATA

Speed, average maximum:
    Road 26 m.p.h. (*41·83 km./h.*).   C.C. 15 m.p.h. (*24·14 km./h.*).
Range of action at average maximum speed (solo): 350 miles (*563 km.*).
Gross power weight ratio (b.h.p. per ton) (solo): 9·2.
Maximum tractive effort, low gear (lb. per ton) (solo): 1,382.
Maximum gradient for stop and restart (solo): 1 in 5.

TECHNICAL DATA

Power Unit
Type: Rolls-Royce, B81, Mk. 5K, gasoline.
Displacement: 6,522 c.c. (398 cu. in.).
Gross B.H.P.: 195 at 3,750 r.p.m.
Nett torque: 308 lb. ft. at 2,150 r.p.m.
Speed limited to: 3,750 r.p.m.
Ignition type: Coil, 24 volt.
Fuel System
Type: Pressure feed.
Type of fuel: Gasoline.
Air cleaner: F.V.R.D.E. oil bath.
Fuel capacity: 98 gallons (*445·5 litres*).
Engine Lubrication
System: Wet sump.
Engine Cooling
System: Pressurised.
Wheels
Rims: 4 piece disc pattern.
Tyres: 15·00″ × 20″ C.C.
Tyre pump: Inflator from air reservoir.
Chains: Non-skid front, overall rear.
Transmission
Clutch: Twin plate.
Gearbox: 4-speed synchromesh, 1 reverse.
Transfer box: 3-speed.

Transmission—*continued*
Transfer box ratios: 1·055 : 1, 1·36 : 1, 2·69 : 1.
Propeller shafts: Hardy Spicer.
Axles: Driven front and rear.
Ratios: Top 14·9 : 1, bottom 190·4 : 1.
Differentials: Two.
Brakes
Foot: Air pressure on all wheels.
Hand: Disc type transmission brake.
Trailer: 2-line air pressure.
Warning device: Pressure gauge.
Steering
System: Cam and roller, hydraulic power assistance.
Turning circle: R.H. 70′ dia. (*21·34 metres*). L.H. 70′ dia. (*21·34 metres*).
Suspension
Front: Single transverse semi-elliptic.
Rear: 2 semi-elliptic.
Towing Attachments
Type: Front, hook. Rear, hook.
Electrical Equipment
Generator: 28 volt 12 amp.
Batteries: 24 volt 60 amp./h.
Suppression: F.V.R.D.E.
Specification 2051, Appendix D1, Schedule B.

MANUFACTURERS

Chassis: LEYLAND MOTORS LTD., Leyland, Lancs.
Recovery Equipment: LEYLAND MOTORS LTD., Leyland, Lancs.
    ROYAL ORDNANCE FACTORIES.

Trailer Recovery (10 ton)

(Project State—In Service)

Description: This trailer has been designed and constructed for the recovery and transportation of all types of vehicles up to and including the 10 ton GS and CT wheeled vehicles and the F.V. 430 series tracked vehicles. It is normally used in conjunction with the Tractor 10 ton 6 × 6 CT Recovery F.V. 1119(A).

F.V. Specification Number: Chassis 9654. Body 9654.

Height: 6′ 3″ (*1·90 m.*).   Length: 23′ 10½″ (*7·28 m.*).
Width: 9′ 0″ (*2·74 m.*).   Wheelbase: 14′ 0″ (*4·27 m.*).
Track: Front 6′ 9″ (*2·06 m.*).   Rear 6′ 9″ (*2·06 m.*).
Weight: Unladen 15,700 lb. (*7,130 kg.*).   Laden 44,240 lb. (*20,067 kg.*).

TECHNICAL DATA

Wheels
Rims: 7·33″ × 20″.
Tyres: 11·00″ × 20″.
Tyre pump: Inflator hose from air reservoir.

Brakes
Service: 2-line air pressure.

Brakes—*continued*
Parking: Mechanical on rear wheels only.

Steering
System: Turntable.

Suspension
Front: Semi-elliptic.
Rear: Semi-elliptic.

MANUFACTURERS

Chassis: RUBERY, OWEN & CO. LTD., Darlaston, Staffs.
J. BROCKHOUSE & CO. LTD., Clydebank, Glasgow.

Trailer Dummy Axle Recovery (10/30 ton)
(Project State—Undergoing User Trials)

Description: The vehicle has a suspended tow capacity of 10 tons, and therefore can be used for the recovery of most vehicles in the up to 30 ton class including Thornycroft Antar. The vehicle has a single unsprung axle fitted with 2 twin wheels and tyres. The casualty is lifted by a jib pivotted on the axle, with a winch, 4-fall reeving, and lifting beam. The casualty is further located by an A-frame which incorporates a pivotted towing eye with automatic catch to facilitate coupling to the casualty. An integral hydraulic system is fitted, powered by a 433 c.c. 4-stroke petrol engine, which operates the winch, moves the jib between lifting and travelling positions, and raises and lowers the A-frame and dolly wheels. Construction throughout is welded rectangular hollow section of high yield steel.

EQUIPMENT

This vehicle is equipped with spare wheel, stowage locker, lifting chains, towing beam, lighting beam for attachment to casualty, and floodlight.

Height: 10′ 7″ (*3·22 m.*).　Length: 12′ 0″ (*3·66 m.*).
Width: 7′ 10″ (*2·39 m.*).　Wheelbase (Axle to towing eye) 10′ 2″ (*3·1 m.*).
Track: 5′ 10″ (*1·78 m.*).
Weight: Unladen 6,400 lb. (*2·900 kg.*).　Laden: 28,800 lb. (*13,100 kg.*).

TECHNICAL DATA

Wheels
Rims: B8·00″ × 15″ 3 piece.
Tyres: 10·00″ × 15″ 14 ply rating.
Tyre pump: By hose from tractor.

Brakes
Trailer:
Service: Two-line air pressure.
Parking: Mechanical hand brake.

MANUFACTURERS

Chassis: Transport Equipment (Thornycroft) Ltd., Basingstoke.

Container Transportable Vehicle Mounted
(1 ton)

(Project State—In Service)

Description: This Container is designed for maximum utilisation for both Army and R.A.F. mobile or static requirements. It is normally transported on a flat platform vehicle but separate facilities are provided to enable it to be readily loaded into aircraft or removed from the vehicle to the ground or on to another vehicle. The Container is framed up from aluminium alloy interlocking, extruded sections externally panelled with aluminium sheet and internally panelled with melamine faced, balanced hardboard. The cavity between the panels is packed with thermal insulating material. The floor is constructed from aluminium sheet and aero-web honeycomb sandwich. Rails are secured to the interior walls for equipment mounting. A door is fitted to the rear of the Container.

Air conditioning equipment can be readily installed using the standard apertures whilst the Container can be pressurised for protection against N.B.C. attack. The Container is shown mounted on a Truck Cargo 3 ton 4 × 4 Bedford. Exhibit No. 47 is an identical Container but is shown demounted and installed with air conditioners.

Height: 6′ 1″ (*1·85 m.*) external, 5′ 8½″ (*1·741 m.*) internal.

Length: 9′ 0½″ (*2·756 m.*) external, 9′ 1¾″ (*2·483 m.*) internal.

Width: 7′ 4″ (*2·235 m*) external, 7′ 11¾″ (*2·127 m*) internal.

Weight: Unladen 1,300 lb. (*589·7 kg.*).   Laden 3,540 lb. (*1605·7 kg.*).

MANUFACTURER AND DESIGNER

MICKLEOVER TRANSPORT LTD., Twyford Works, Park Royal, London, N.W.10.

Container Transportable Vehicle Mounted (3 ton)

(Project State—Under Development)

Description: This Container is a variant of Exhibit No. 46 (CB 305). It is installed with a prototype screened compartment and a variety of air conditioning and NBC protection equipment as a demonstration installation.

Height: 6′ 3″ (*1·905 m*) external, 5′ 10·3″ (*1·78 m*) internal.
Length: 15′ 4″ (*4·67 m.*) external, 14′ 1·6″ (*4·31 m.*) internal.
Width: 8′ 3″ (*2·51 m*) external, 7′ 7·6″ (*2·32 m*) internal.
Weight: Unladen 2,100 lb. (*952 kg.*).   Laden 8,820 lb. (*4,000 kg.*).

Installation includes:

Air conditioner No. 52H Mk. 1: Power supply 250 v. 50 c.p.s. single phase.
Cooling capacity 9,800 B.Th.U./hour.
Heating capacity 2,000 watts.

This unit can also be supplied powered by 415 v. 50 c.p.s. 3 phase.

Air conditioner No. 55 Mk. 2: Power supply 250 v. 50 c.p.s. single phase.
Cooling capacity 9,500 B.Th.U./hour.
Heating capacity 2,000 watts.

This unit can also be supplied powered by 415 v. 50 c.p.s. 3 phase.

Dehumidifier Space No. 1 Mk. 1/1: Power supply 250 v. 50 c.p.s. single phase.

Dehumidifier Space No. 2 Mk. 1: Power supply 250 v. 50 c.p.s. single phase.

Mock-up models of new range of 400 c.p.s. Air Conditioners:

  (a) 9,000 B.Th.U./hour cooling capacity unit.
  (b) 15,000 B.Th.U./hour cooling capacity unit. This unit will also be available powered by 50 c.p.s. supply.

continued overleaf

Penthouse:

A standard penthouse is fitted to this Container. It is shown heated by a 23,000 B.Th.U./hour petrol burning heater.

Screened Cubical:
Attenuation 60db in frequency range 3 to 1,000 m/c.

FIRMS CONCERNED

MARSHALL OF CAMBRIDGE (ENGINEERING) LTD., Cambridge.
GLOSTER SARO LTD., Beaumaris, Anglesey, North Wales.
TEMPERATURE LTD., Burlington Road, Fulham, S.W.6.
WESTAIR DYNAMICS LTD., St. Helens Auckland, Co. Durham.
R. S. & P. (ENGINEERS) LTD., Western Avenue, Ealing, W.5.
SMITHS INDUSTRIES LTD., Witney, Oxon.

Container Transportable (3 ton)

(Project State—In Service)

Description: This Container is designed for maximnm utilisation for both Army and R.A.F. mobile or static requirements. It is normally transported on a flat platform vehicle but separate facilities are provided to enable it to be readily loaded into aircraft or moved from vehicle to vehicle or to the ground. The Container is of aluminium lightweight fully enclosed construction thermally insulated and internally lined with melamine faced hardboard. Rails are secured to the interior of the walls for equipment mounting, and recessed ducting is provided for internal wiring. The Container is made up in a module system which enables doors, windows and apertures to be installed in a variety of positions. Airconditioning equipment can be readily installed using the standard apertures, whilst the Container can be pressurised for protection against NBC attack. Standard penthouses are available with this Container.

continued overleaf

The exhibit shows the Container supported on high lift jacks with the truck removed and is also shown mounted on a Truck Cargo Airportable 3 ton 4 × 4 Bedford F.V. 13142 (A).

F.V. Specification Number: Body 9707.

Height: External 6′ 3″ (*1·905 m.*). Internal 5′ 10·3″ (*1·78 m.*).

Length: External 15′ 4″ (*4·67 m.*). Internal 14′ 1·6″ (*4·31 m.*).

Width: External 8′ 3″ (*2·51 m.*). Internal 7′ 7·6″ (*2·32 m.*).

Weight: Unladen 2,100 lb. (*952 kg.*). Laden 8,820 lb. (*4,000 kg.*).

DESIGN

MARSHALL OF CAMBRIDGE (ENGINEERING) LTD.

MANUFACTURERS

MARSHALL OF CAMBRIDGE (ENGINEERING) LTD.
GLOSTER SARO LTD.

Container Transportable (1 ton)

For full particulars see Exhibit No. 44.

Container Equipment Transportable
(6' x 6' x 6')

Description: This Container is of similar construction to the 'Container Airportable 1 ton CB.101', it varies in that it has a flat roof and its dimensions are reduced.

Height: Approx. 6' 0" (*1·83 m.*).　Length: 6' 0" (*1·83 m.*). Approx.
Width: Approx. 6' 0" (*1·83 m.*).
Weight: Unladen 850 lb. (*396 kg.*).　Laden: 3,090 lb. (*1,400 kg.*).

MANUFACTURER AND DESIGNER

MICKLEOVER TRANSPORT LTD., Twyford Works, Park Royal, London, N.W.10.

Trailer Transporter Container Body
(Bloodhound LCP 5 ton)

(Project State—In Service)

Description: This standard 5 ton 4 wheeled trailer is fitted with a special flat platform and underslung lockers. The platform and lockers are mainly constructed from aluminium alloy sections. The trailer, whilst primarily intended for the carriage of Bloodbound Mk. 2 LCP Body Container is also used as a general load carrier for the Bloodhound System, and as a loading platform to enable System Equipment to be 'fork lifted' and then 'rolled' onto a transfer loader for airporting. For this purpose steady jacks, roller conveyors and a hand winch are supplied.

F.V. Specification Number: Chassis 9301. Body 9704.

Height: 3′ 9″ (*1·14 m.*) Unladen.
Length: 18′ 5½″ (*5·63 m.*) platform, 27′ 0″ (*8·22 m.*) including tow bar.

Width: 8′ 0″ (*2·44 m.*). Wheelbase: 12′ 11″ (*3·94 m.*).
Track: Front 6′ 7″ (*2·02 m.*). Rear: 6′ 7″ (*2·02 m.*).
Weight: Unladen 7,512 lb. (*3,870 kg.*) fully kitted. Laden 21,056 lb.
(*9,650 kg.*).

TECHNICAL DATA

Wheels
Rims: B8·00″ × 15″.
Tyres: 10·00″ × 15″ standard
tread.

Brakes
Service: 2-line air pressure on all
wheels.
Parking: Screw operated, on rear
wheels.

Steering
System: Ackermann type.
Turning circle: 55′ R.H. (*16·8 m.*).

Steering—*continued*
55′ L.H. (16·8 *m.*).

Suspension
Front / Semi-elliptic springs.
Rear \ Spring clamps at all spring
stations to assist in airporting.
Shock absorbers: Telescopic hydraulic.

Towing Attachments
Type: Front: Standard eye. Rear:
Hook.

MANUFACTURERS

Chassis: RUBERY, OWEN & CO. LTD.
Body: MICKLEOVER TRANSPORT LTD.

Container Transportable, Electronic Repair, SAGW No. 2, Vehicle Mounted (3 ton)

(Project State—In production)

Description: The construction of this container is based on the 'Container Airportable 3 ton CB.305' and it is fitted for the repair and maintenance of the electronic equipment of the SAGW No. 2 system. Its main feature is an all welded aluminium screened cubicle in which are tested and set up repaired electronic units. A standard penthouse is provided and can be attached to the right hand side of the container for storage of equipment or an extension of working space. This is typical of the installations being built into the standard containers and demonstrates the use of its unit features. The container is shown on a Truck Cargo Airportable 3 ton 4 × 4 Bedford F.V. 13142 (A).

Height: 6′ 3″ (*1·93 m.*).   Length: 16′ 1″ (*5 m.*).
Width: 8′ 0″ (*2·48 m.*).   Weight: Laden 8,960 lb. (*4,070 kg.*).

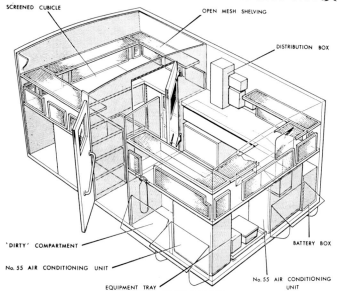

SCREENED CUBICLE

OPEN MESH SHELVING

DISTRIBUTION BOX

'DIRTY' COMPARTMENT

No. 55 AIR CONDITIONING UNIT

BATTERY BOX

EQUIPMENT TRAY

No. 55 AIR CONDITIONING UNIT

SPECIAL FEATURES

Screened Cubicle Characteristic
60 db attenuation in a frequency range of 3 to 1000 m/c.

Airconditioning
Two No. 55 Mk. 1/1 manually controlled.

Dehumidified
One dehumidifier space No. 1 Mk. 1.

Fittings
Melamime surfaced benches around the container walls. Drawers and cupboards positioned beneath the benches. Shelves positioned above the benches. Stowage of test equipment is facilitated by the use of expanded metal panelled shelves and frames with straps.

Electrical
415 volt 3 phase 50 c.p.s. supply.
12 volt d.c. for emergency lighting and testing.
12 volt battery charger.
Flourescent lighting, tungstan bench lights.
13 amp 215 volt 50 c.p.s. power sockets.

DESIGN

Body: MARSHALL OF CAMBRIDGE (ENGINEERING) LTD., Cambridge.
Electrical: R. S. & P. (ENGINEERS) LTD., Cinimon Parade, Western Avenue, W.5.

MANUFACTURERS

Body: MARSHALL OF CAMBRIDGE (ENGINEERING) Ltd., Cambridge.
Airconditioning: WESTAIR DYNAMICS LTD., St. Helens Auckland, Co. Durham.

Container Transportable Radar Repair FA
No. 8 Mk. 1 Vehicle Mounted (3 ton)
(Project State—In Service)

Description: The construction of this Container is based on the 'Container Airportable 3 ton CB.305' it differs in that it has a detachable roof. This feature facilitates installation of the 'Slave Radar' rack and provides good head room for operators. Airporting in the 'Argosy' aircraft is achieved by removal of the roof. Equipment is installed to enable testing, fault diagnosis and repair of radar units in an air-conditioned atmosphere. The radar vehicle under repair can be housed in a penthouse attached to the side of the Container. The Container shown is mounted on a Truck Cargo Airportable 3 ton 4 × 4 Bedford F.V.13142A.

F.V. Specification 9697.

Height: With roof 6′ 7·5″ (*1·97 m.*). With roof removed 6′ 1″ (*1·855 m.*).
Length: 15′ (*4·45 m.*).   Width: 8′ 3″ (*2·52 m.*).
Weight: Laden 8,960 lb. (*4,070 kg.*).

SPECIAL FEATURES

Roof
Detachable in three sections.

Stowage Locker
Full width and height of container across front bulkhead.

Benches
Melamime surfaced.

Drawers
Positioned beneath benches.

Cupboards
Two, the full height of the container with facilities for stowing the maximum variety of test equipment.

Airconditioning
One Type 52H Mk. 2.

Airconditioning—*continued*
One Type 55 Mk. 1/1.
Both with manual control.

Dehumidifier
One Dehumidifier Space No. 1 Mk. 1.

Electrical
210 volt 3 phase 400 c.p.s. for radar equipment.
415 volt 3 phase 50 c.p.s. for airconditioning.
12 and 24 volt d.c. with duel voltage battery charger for emergency lighting and collimating equipment, fluorescent lighting and tungstan bench lights.

DESIGN

Body: MARSHALL OF CAMBRIDGE (ENGINEERING) LTD., Cambridge.
Electrical: R. S. & P. (ENGINEERS) LTD., Cinema Parade, Western Avenue, W.5.

MANUFACTURERS

Body: MARSHALL OF CAMBRIDGE (ENGINEERING) LTD., Cambridge.
Airconditioning: WESTAIR DYNAMICS LTD., St. Helens, Auckland, Co. Durham.
TEMPERATURE LTD., Burlington Road, Fulham, S.W.6.

Container Body (Aircon B)

(Project State—In Service)

Description: This Container is used to house a variety of electronic and telecommunication equipment for Army and R.A.F. use in both mobile and static roles. It is normally transported as a trailer on a detachable two wheeled running gear which will retract to lower the Container to the ground and provide for easy loading into aircraft. The Container is of stressed skin steel construction spot welded to a steel framework. The inner panels are of tempered hardboard and the cavity between the skins is filled with fibre glass thermal insulation. This Container can be provided with doors in one or both end frames; windows can be positioned in both sides or in the doors as required.

Dimension Container only

Height: Internal 5′ 5·25″ (*1·652 m*.).   External 5′ 10″ (*1·78 m*.).
Width: Internal 5′ 1″ (*1·55 m*.).   External 5′ 5″ (*1·65 m*.).
Length: Internal 5′ 10″ (*1·78 m*.).   External 6′ 2″ (*1·88 m*.).

Overall Dimensions on Running Gear including Towbar

Height: 7′ 1·75 ″ (*2·175 m*.).   Width: 8′ 4·75″ (*2·548 m*.).
Length: 12′ 1½″ (*3·7 m*.).

Weight Container only

Unladen: 900 lb. (*408 kg*.).   Laden 3,900 lb. (*1,770 kg*.).

Weight of Running Gear

450 lb. per side (*204 kg*.).   Towbar weighs 120 lb. (*54·6 kg*.).

Suspension

Coil spring telescopic hydraulic shock absorbers.

Brakes

Drum brakes operated by override mechanism.

Wheels

Rims: Disc 5·00 F.   Tyres: 7·00 × 16″.

Electrical Equipment

Lighting: 24 volt to full road traffic requirements.

MANUFACTURERS

AIRTECH LTD., Haddenham, Bucks.

Tractor Wheeled Semi Trailer
(Thornycroft Antar Mk. 3, 30 ton 6 x 4)

(Project State—In Service)

Description: This vehicle is the prime mover for the 50 ton and 60 ton semi-trailers FV.3011 and FV.3001 respectively. It embodies an 8 cylinder CI supercharged engine. A 20 ton winch is fitted for loading disabled AFV's and also for self-recovery operations.

F.V. Specification Number: Chassis 9207.

Height: 10′ 4″ (*3·15 m.*).   Length: 28′ 6½″ (*8·70 m.*).
Width: 10′ 6″ (*3·20 m.*).   Wheelbase: 16′ 0″ (*4·88 m.*).
Track: Front 7′ 4½″ (*2·25 m.*).   Rear 7′ 6¼″ (*2·35 m.*).
Weight: Solo 48,272 lb. (*21,896 kg.*).

PERFORMANCE DATA

Speed, average maximum:
Road 20 m.p.h. (*32·18 km.h.*).
Range of action at average maximum speed (fully laden train): 436 miles (*702 km.*).
Gross Power weight ratio (b.h.p. per ton) (fully laden train): 3·16.
Maximum tractive effort, lower gear (lb. per ton) (fully laden train): 590.
Maximum gradient for stop and restart (fully laden train): 1 in 6.

TECHNICAL DATA

Power Unit
Type: Rolls-Royce C8 SFL–843.
Displacement: 16,200 c.c. (990·2 cu. in.).
Gross B.H.P.: 333 at 2,100 r.p.m.
Nett torque: 935 lb. ft. at 1,300 r.p.m.
Governed speed: 2,100 r.p.m.
Ignition type: Compression.

Fuel System
Type: Pressure feed.
Type of fuel: Diesel.
Air cleaner: F.V.R.D.E. Oil bath.
Fuel capacity: 200 gallons (*910 litres*).

Engine Lubrication
System: Semi-dry sump.

Engine Cooling
System: Pressurised.

Wheels
Rims: 4-piece disc type.
Tyres: 14·00″ × 24″ C.C.
Tyre pump: Inflator from air compressor.
Chains: Overall tracks rear.

Transmission
Clutch: Twin plate, air assisted.
Gearbox: 6-speed, 1 reverse.
Transfer box: 6-speed, 1 reverse.
Propeller shafts: Hardy Spicer.

Transmission—*continued*
Axles: Driven rear only.
Ratios: top 9·03 : 1, bottom 139 : 1.
Differentials: Three.
Differential locks: Inter-axle lock on rear bogie.

Brakes
Foot: Air pressure on all wheels.
Hand: Mechanical, air assisted, rear wheels only.
Trailer: 2-line air pressure.
Warning device: Pressure gauge.

Steering
System: Cam and double roller, hydraulic assisted.
Turning circle: R.H. 66′ (*20·12 metres*). L.H. 66′ (*20·12 metres*).

Suspension
Front- Semi-elliptic.
Rear: Semi-elliptic.

Towing Attachments
Type: pintle. Rear, hook.

Electrical Equipment
Generator: 28 volt 40 amp.
Batteries: 24 volt 300 amp./h.
Suppression: F.V.R.D.E.
Specification 2051, Appendix D1, Schedule B.

MANUFACTURERS

Chassis: TRANSPORT EQUIPMENT (THORNYCROFT) LTD., Basingstoke, Hants.

ALTERNATIVE ROLES

Tractor for full trailer—with temporary ballast body fitted.

Semi-Trailer Tank Transporter (50 ton)

(Project State—In Service)

Description: This semi-trailer together with the Tractor Wheeled 30 ton 6 × 4 Antar, Exhibit No. 53, forms a tank transportation train for the logistic movement of armoured fighting vehicles or stores of up to 50 tons gross weight. Winch rope guide rollers are fitted to the front and rear of the semi-trailer to facilitate loading of vehicle casualties.

F.V. Specification Number: Chassis 9180.

Height: 10′ 1½″ (*3·09 m.*).   Length: 39′ 1½″ (*11·93 m.*).
Width: 11′ 0″ (*3·35 m.*).   Wheelbase (to king pin): 28′ 6½″ (*8·70 m.*).
Track: Inner 2′ 10½″ (*0·88 m.*).   Outer 8′ 10″ (*2·70 m.*).
Weight: Unladen 36,064 lb. (*16,359 kg.*).   Laden 148,064 lb. (*67,162 kg.*).

TECHNICAL DATA

Wheels
Rims: 4-piece disc type.
Tyres: 12·00″ × 20″ standard tread.
Tyre Pump: Inflator from air reservoir.

Brakes
Service: 2-line air pressure/hydraulic system.
Parking: Mechanical/hydraulic

Brakes—*continued*
hand operated.

Jacking
Manually operated hydraulic jacks.

Suspension
Unsprung walking beam.

Towing Attachments
King Pin Size: 3½″ dia. (*0.089 m.*).

MANUFACTURERS

GKN Group Services Ltd., FVD Division, Smethwick, 40, Staffs.
J. Sankey & Sons Ltd., Manor Works, Ettingshall, Wolverhampton.
Taskers of Andover (1932) Ltd., Andover, Hants.

Tractor Wheeled General Service with Ballast body (Thornycroft Antar Mk. 3, 30 ton 6 x 4)

(Project State—In Service)

Description: This vehicle is the tractor for full trailer version of the Antar Mk. 3. In this role the vehicle is the prime mover for towing the 50 ton trailer transporter—F.V.3601. The temporary ballast body is easily removable to enable conversion to the tractor for semi-trailer role to be carried out with a minimum of effort.

F.V. Specification Number: Chassis 9207. Body 9683.

Height: 10′ 4″ (*3·15 m.*).   Length: 28′ 6½″ (*8·70 m.*).
Width: 10′ 6″ (*3·20 m.*).   Wheelbase: 16′ 0″ (*4·88 m.*).
Track: Front 7′ 4½″ (*2·25 m.*).   Rear: 7′ 6¼″ (*2·35 m.*).
Weight: Unladen 50,792 lb. (*23,040 kg.*).   Laden: 80,640 *lb.* (*36,578 kg.*).

PERFORMANCE DATA

Speed, average maximum, road: 20 m.p.h. (*32·18 km./h.*).
Range of action at average maximum speed (fully laden train): 436 mile (*702 km.*).
Gross power weight ratio (b.h.p. per ton) (fully laden train): 3·22.
Maximum tractive effort, low gear (lb. per ton) (fully laden train): 600
Maximum gradient for stop and restart (fully laden train): 1 in 6.

TECHNICAL DATA

Power Unit
Type: Rolls-Royce, C8SFL-843.
Displacement: 16,200 c.c. (990·2 cu. in.)
Gross B.H.P.: 333 at 2,100 r.p.m.
Nett torque: 935 lb. ft. at 1,300 r.p.m.
Governed speed: 2,100 r.p.m.
Ignition type: Compression.
Fuel System
Type: Pressure feed.
Type of fuel: Diesel.
Air cleaner: F.V.R.D.E. oil bath.
Fuel capacity: 200 gallons (*910 litres*).
Engine Lubrication
System: Semi-dry sump.
Engine Cooling
System: Pressurised.
Wheels
Rims: 4-piece disc type.
Tyres: 14·00″ × 24″ C.C.
Tyre pump: Inflator from air compressor.
Chains: Overall tracks rear.
Transmission
Clutch: Twin plate, air assisted.
Gearbox: 6-speed and reverse.
Transfer Box: 6-speed and reverse.

Propeller shafts: Hardy Spicer.
Axles: Driven rear only.
Ratios: Top 9·03 : 1, bottom 139 : 1.
Differentials: Three.
Differential Locks: Inter-axle lock on rear bogie.
Brakes
Foot: Air pressure on all wheels.
Hand: Mechanical, air assisted, rear wheels only.
Trailer: 2-line air pressure.
Warning device: Pressure gauge.
Steering
System: Cam and double roller, hydraulic assistance.
Turning circle: R.H. 66′ dia. (*20·12 metres*). L.H. 66′ dia. (*20·12 metres*).
Suspension
Front: Semi-elliptic.
Rear: Semi-elliptic.
Towing Attachments
Type: Front, pintle. Rear, hook.
Electrical Equipment
Generator: 28 volt 40 amp.
Batteries: 24 volt 300 amp./h.
Suppression: F.V.R.D.E.
Specification 2051, Appendix D1, Schedule B.

MANUFACTURERS

Chassis: ⎱ TRANSPORT EQUIPMENT (THORNYCROFT) LTD., Basingstoke,
Body: ⎰ Hants.

ALTERNATIVE ROLES

Tractor for semi-trailer.

Trailer Tank Transporter No. 1 Mk. 3 (50 ton)

(Project State—In Service)

Description: This trailer transporter together with the Tractor Wheeled General Service (30 ton 6 × 4 Antar), Exhibit No. 54, forms a transportation train for the road movement of armoured fighting vehicles and specialised equipment of up to 50 tons gross weight. The loading platform is decked in to permit the carriage of general cargo.

F.V. Specification Number: Chassis 9062. Body 9062.

Height: 7′ 3″ (*2·21 m.*). Length: (including drawbar) 33′ 6″ (*10·21 m.*).
Width: 10′ 6″ (*3·20 m.*).   Wheelbase: 15′ 0″ (*4·57 m.*).
Track: Outer 7′ 10½″ (*2·40 m.*).   Inner 2′ 7″ (*0·79 m.*).
Weight: Unladen 41,100 lb. (*18,643 kg.*). Laden 153,100 lb. (*69·446 kg.*).

TECHNICAL DATA

Wheels
Rims: 3-piece disc type.
Tyres: 36″ × 8″ standard tread.
Tyre Pump: Inflator connected to air reservoir.

Brakes
Service: 2-line air pressure.
Parking: Mechanical, hand operated, rear wheels only.

Jacking
Manually operated hydraulic jacks.

Steering
System: Turntable.

Suspension
Front: Unsprung walking beam.
Rear: Unsprung walking beam.

MANUFACTURERS

Chassis: R. A. DYSON & CO. LTD., Grafton Street, Liverpool 8.
Body: CRANES (DEREHAM) LTD., Dereham, Norfolk.

Tractor Wheeled Semi-Trailer
(Scammel 20 ton 6 x 6)

(Project State—In Service)

Description: This tractor is the motive power unit for the semi-trailer 30 ton RE plant. It is of the 6-wheel drive pattern and possesses a good cross-country performance. The cab accommodates two passengers in addition to the driver. The winch is rated at 15 ton.

F.V. Specification Number: Chassis 9176. Body 9603.

Height: 10′ 2″ (*3·10 m.*).   Length: 24′ 5½″ (*7·46 m.*).
Width: 9′ 4″ (*2·85 m.*).   Wheelbase: 15′ 9″ (*4·80 m.*).
Track: Front: 6′ 11″ (*2·11 m.*).   Rear: 6′ 7⅞″ (*2·1 m.*).
Weight: Solo 32,368 lb. (*14,682 kg.*).

PERFORMANCE DATA

Speed, average maximum:
  Road 25 m.p.h. (*40·23 km./h.*).
  C.C. 12 m.p.h. (*19·30 km./h.*).
Range of action at average maximum specd: 500 miles (*805 km.*).
Gross power weight ratio (b.h.p. per ton) (solo): 12·8.
Maximum tractive effort, low gear (lb. per ton) (solo): 3,077.
Maximum gradient for stop and restart (fully laden train): 1 in 5.

TECHNICAL DATA

Power Unit
Type: Rolls-Royce, C6 NFL-140.
Displacement: 12,170 c.c. (742·6 cu. in.).
Gross B.H.P.: 184 at 2,100 r.p.m.
Nett torque: 490 lb. ft. at 1,400 r.p.m.
Governed speed: 2,100 r.p.m.
Ignition type: Compression.
Fuel System
Type: Pressure feed.
Type of fuel: Diesel.
Air Cleaner: F.V.R.D.E. oil bath.
Fuel capacity: 110 gallons (*500 litres*).
Engine Lubrication
System: Dry sump.
Engine Cooling
System: Pressurised.
Wheels
Rims: 4-piece disc.
Tyres: 14·00″ × 20″ C.C.
Tyre pump: Inflator from air reservoir.
Chains: Non-skid front and rear.
Transmission
Clutch: Single plate.
Gearbox: 6-speed, constant mesh and reverse.
Transfer box: 2-speed.

Transmission—*continued*
Transfer box ratios: 1·323 : 1, 2·535 : 1.
Propeller shafts: Hardy Spicer.
Axles: Driven front and rear.
Ratios: Top 8·436 : 1, bottom 170·25 : 1.
Differentials: Three.
Brakes
Foot: Air pressure on all wheels.
Hand: Mechanical and 'hill holder'.
Trailer: 2-line air pressure.
Warning device: Pressure gauge.
Steering
System: Cam and double roller, air pressure assistance.
Turning circle: R.H. 80′ 6″ dia. (*24·54 metres*). L.H. 83′ 6″ dia. (*25·45 metres*).
Suspension
Front: Single transverse semi-elliptic.
Rear: 2 semi-elliptic.
Towing Attachments
Type: Front, hook. Rear, hook.
Electrical Equipment
Generator: 28 volt 25 amp.
Batteries: 24 volt 150 amp./h.
Suppression: F.V.R.D.E.
Specification 2051, Appendix D1, Schedule B.

MANUFACTURERS

Chassis: ⎫
Body: ⎭ SCAMMELL LORRIES LTD., Watford, Herts.

ALTERNATIVE ROLES

Tractor for 50 ton tank transporter.

Tractor Wheeled General Service
(Scammel 20 ton 6 x 6)

(Project State—In Service)

Description: This tractor is used for towing 30-ton full trailers or for transportation of general cargo and engineering equipment. It has 6-wheel drive and is capable of negotiating landing craft ramps but is not wade-proofed. The cab accommodates two passengers in addition to the driver. The winch is rated at 15 ton.

F.V. Specification Number: Chassis 9220. Body 9220.

Height: 10′ 9″ (*3·28 m.*).   Length: 25′ 1½″ (*7·66 m.*).
Width: 9′ 4½″ (*2·86 m.*).   Wheelbase: 15′ 9″ (*4·80 m.*).
Track: Front 6′ 11″ (*2·11 m.*).   Rear: 6′ 7⅞″ (*2·1 m.*).
Weight: Unladen 37,527 lb. (*17,022 kg.*).   Laden: 59,360 lb. (*26,926 kg.*).

PERFORMANCE DATA

Speed, average maximum:
    Road 25 m.p.h. (*40·23 km./h.*).
    C.C. 12 m.p.h. (*19·30 km./h.*).
Range of action at average maximum speed: 500 miles (*805 km.*).
Gross power weight ratio (b.h.p. per ton) (laden solo): 6·95.
Maximum tractive effort, low gear (lb. per ton (laden solo): 1,672
(100% efficiency on nett torque).
Maximum gradient for stop and restart (solo): 1 in 3.

TECHNICAL DATA

Power Unit
Type: Rolls-Royce, C6 NFL-142A.
Displacement: 12,170 c.c. (742·6 cu. in.).
Gross B.H.P.: 184 at 2,100 r.p.m.
Nett torque: 490 lb. ft. at 1,400 r.p.m.
Governed speed: 2,100 r.p.m.
Ignition type: Compression.
Fuel System
Type: Pressure feed.
Type of fuel: Diesel.
Air cleaner: F.V.R.D.E. oil bath.
Fuel capacity: 110 gallons (*500 litres*).
Engine Lubrication
System: Wet sump.
Engine Cooling
System: Pressurised.
Wheels
Rims: 4-piece disc.
Tyres: 14·00" × 20" C.C.
Tyre pump: Inflator from air reservoir.
Chains: Non-skid front and rear.
Transmission
Clutch: Single plate.
Gearbox: 6-speed, constant mesh, 1 reverse.
Transfer box: 2-speed.

Transfer box ratios: 1·323 : 1, 2·535 : 1.
Propeller shafts: Hardy Spicer.
Axles: Driven front and rear.
Ratios: Top 8·436 : 1, bottom 170·25 : 1.
Differentials: Three.
Brakes
Foot: Air pressure on all wheels.
Hand: Mechanical and 'hill holder'.
Trailer: 2-line air pressure.
Warning device: Pressure gauge.
Steering
System: Cam and double roller, air pressure assistance.
Turning Circle: R.H. 80' 6" dia. (*24·54 metres*). L.H. 83' 6" (*25·45 metres*).
Suspension
Front: Single transverse semi-elliptic.
Rear: 2 semi-elliptic.
Towing Attachments
Type: Front, hook. Rear, hook.
Electrical Equipment
Generator: 28 volt 25 amp.
Batteries: 24 volt 150 amp./h.
Suppression: F.V.R.D.E.
Specification 2051, Appendix DI, Schedule B.

MANUFACTURERS

Chassis: ⎫
Body: ⎭ SCAMMELL LORRIES LTD., Watford, Herts.

ALTERNATIVE ROLES

Tractor for 50 ton tank transporter.

121

Trenching Machine Wheeled
(4 x 4 Thornycroft)
(Security Classification: Unclassified)

Description: This vehicle has been developed by the Military Engineering Experimental Establishment with the object of providing an equipment which can dig a variety of slit trenches and pits rapidly in all types of soil. It is fully mobile, suitable for use over rough ground, and it is airportable. The machine comprises a modified Thornycroft 'Nubian' 4 × 4 chassis which carries a digging head and transverse soil disposal conveyor assembly on twin, traversable boom arms. This permits the digging head to operate off the chassis centre line for the excavation of offset trenches and pits wider than the cutting jib. The jib carries three cutting chains which are hydraulically driven from the vehicle engine. The road wheels are also hydraulically driven during the digging operation to give creep cutting speeds.

Height: (travelling condition) 8′ 6″ (*2·59 m.*).   Length: 22′ 9″ (*6·93 m.*).
Width: 7′ 8″ (*2.34 m.*).   Wheelbase: 11′ 8″ (*3·56 m.*).
Track: Front 6′ 2″ (*1·88 m.*).   Rear 6′ 3¼″ (*1·91 m.*).
Weight: 20,496 lb. (*9,297 kg.*).

PERFORMANCE DATA

Speed, average maximum:
　　Road 43 m.p.h. (*69 km./h.*).　C.C. 20 m.p.h. (*32 km./h.*).
Range of action at average maximum speed: 400 miles (*644 km.*).
Gross power weight ratio (b.h.p. per ton): 23.
Maximum tractive effort, low gear (lb. per ton): 1290.
Maximum climbing ability: 1 in 2.
Maximum gradient for stop and restart: 1 in 3.

TECHNICAL DATA

Power Unit
Type: Rolls Royce, B81, Mk. 7D, Gasoline.
Displacement: 6,522 c.c. (398 cu. in.)
Gross B.H.P.: 210 at 3,200 r.p.m.
Nett torque: 320 lb. ft. at 2,250 r.p.m.
Speed limited to: 3,200 r.p.m.
Ignition type: Coil, 24 volts.
Fuel System
Type: Lift pump.
Type of fuel: Gasoline.
Air cleaner: Dry, self cleaning.
Fuel capacity: 50 gallons (*227 litres*)
Engine Lubrication
System: Wet sump.
Engine Cooling
System: Pressurised.
Wheels
Rims: B8·0″ × 20″.
Tyres: 12·00″ × 20″/14″ ply.
Tyre pump: Inflator hose from vehicle air system.
Transmission
Clutch: Twin dry plate, 12 in. (*30·5 mm.*) dia.
Gearbox: 4-speed constant mesh and reverse.
Transfer box: 2-speed constant mesh.
Transfer box ratios: 1·26 : 1 and 2·14 : 1.
Propeller shafts: Hardy Spicer.
Axles: Driven front and rear.
Ratios: Top 9·43 : 1 bottom 66·9 : 1.
Differentials: Two.

Hydraulics
Chain drive: Pump. Lucas Hydrostatic, swash plate, Type IP 3000/DB2. Motors. Lucas Hydrostatic, swash plate, Type IM 1000/DB2.
Creep/Winch drive: Pump. Lucas Hydrostatic, swash plate, Type IP 500/DB1. Motors. Hamworthy gear type.
Rams and conveyor: Pump. Hamworthy gear type. Motors. (Conveyor) Hamworthy gear type.
Brakes
Foot: Air/hydraulic.
Hand: Mechanical to rear wheels.
Warning device: Air pressure gauge.
Steering
System: Cam and double roller.
Turning circle: R.H. 57′ (*17·37 metres*). L.H. 57′ dia. (*17·37 metres*).
Suspension
Front: Semi-elliptic.
Rear: Semi-elliptic.
Shock absorbers: Four.
Towing attachments
Type: Front, eyes.
Winch: Boughton. Hydraulic drive. Forward creep assistance only.
Electrical Equipment
Generator: 24 volt, 12 amp.
Batteries: 2 × 12 volt No. 1 Mk. 2/1 40 A.H.
Suppression: F.V.R.D.E.
Specification 2051, Appendix D1, Schedule B.

MANUFACTURER

Chassis:
Body: } TRANSPORT EQUIPMENT (THORNYCROFT) LTD., Basingstoke.

Truck Fire Fighting—Airfield Crash Rescue
(Rover, ¾ ton 4 x 4)
(Project State—In Service)

Description: This vehicle has been developed to meet the requirements of M.O.D. (R.A.F.) for a vehicle for immediate rescue from crashed aircraft, to deal with aircraft wheel brake fires, and to act as a light auxiliary fire truck to escort aircraft at dispersals. The vehicle is based on the current commercial specification for the Landrover 109″ wheelbase Pick-up Truck. Changes have been made to the commercial specification to render the vehicle more suitable for Service use. These include such items as, W.D. pattern divided wheels, tyres with C.C. tread, oil cooler and eight-bladed fan, special towing attachment and strengthened rear cross member, modified suspension, F.V. pattern lights, brush-guard to protect front of vehicle, heavy duty front bumper, safety harness for crew members. The fire fighting equipment includes, two high pressure dry powder chemical extinguishers with discharge hoses and nozzles, ladder, saws—hand and compressed air operated, asbestos blankets and gloves, etc. The vehicle is also equipped with a high power searchlight and a site illuminating lamp.

F.V. Specification Number: Chassis 9255. Body 9255.

Equipment: To M.O.A. requirements.
Height: 8' 3" (*2·52 m.*). Length: 15' 3" (*4·65 m.*).
Width: 5' 7½" (*1·72 m.*). Wheelbase: 9' 1" (*2·77 m.*).
Track: Front 4' 3½" (*1·31 m.*). Rear 4' 3½" (*1·31 m.*).
Weight: Unladen 5,000 lb. (*2,270 kg.*). Laden: 5,800 lb. (*2,640 kg.*).

PERFORMANCE DATA

Speed, average maximum:
  Road 45 m.p.h. (*72·4 km./h.*). C.C. 15 m.p.h. (*24·1 km./h.*).
Range of action at average maximum speed: 140 miles (*225 km.*).
Gross power weight ratio (b.h.p. per ton): 29·8.
Maximum tractive effort, low gear (lb. per ton): 1,500.
Maximum climbing ability: 1 in 3.
Maximum gradient for stop and restart: 1 in 3.

TECHNICAL DATA

Power Unit
Type: Rover, 2¼ litre, gasoline.
Displacement: 2,286 c.c. (139 cu. in.).
Gross B.H.P.: 77 at 4,250 r.p.m.
Nett torque: 116 lb. ft. at 1,500 r.p.m.
Ignition type: Coil, 12 volt.
Fuel System
Type: Mechanical lift pump.
Type of fuel: Gasoline.
Air cleaner: Oil bath with pre-cleaner.
Fuel capacity: 10 gallons (Imp.)
(45·5 *litres*).
Engine Lubrication
System: Wet sump.
Engine Cooling
System: Pressurised.
Wheels
Rims: 5·50"E × 16" W.D. divided
type (F.V.84930).
Tyres: 7·50" × 16", 6 P.R. light truck
with C.C. tread pattern.
Tyre pump: Manual.
Chains: Commercial.
Transmission
Clutch: Enclosed S.D.P. 9" (*0·228
metres*) dia.
Gearbox: 4-speed and reverse (syn-
chromesh on 3rd and 4th gears).
Transfer box: 2-speed.
Transfer box ratios: 1·148 : 1 and
2·400 : 1.

Propeller shafts: Telescopic with
Hookes couplings.
Axles: Spiral bevel front and rear.
Ratios: Top, 5·400 : 1, bottom
40·600 : 1.
Differentials: Two.
Brakes
Foot: Hydraulic, all wheels, drum
type.
Hand: Mechanical, transmission,
drum type.
Steering
System: Ackermann.
Turning circle: 50' max. (15·25
metres).
Suspension
Front: Semi-elliptic leaf springs.
Rear: Semi-elliptic leaf springs.
Shock absorbers: Hydraulic, tele-
scopic double acting type.
Towing Attachments
Type: Front, provision only. Rear,
special, jaw and pin type.
Electrical Equipment
Generator: 12 volt D.C.
Batteries: Vehicle 12 volt (lead/acid)
51 A.H. capacity.
Equipment: 12 volt (lead/acid) 100
A.H. capacity.
Suppression: F.V.R.D.E. Specifica-
tion 2051, Schedule B, Appendix D1.

MANUFACTURERS

Chassis: ⎫ THE ROVER CO. LTD., Meteor Works,
Body: ⎭ Solihull, Warwickshire.
Equipment: FOAMITE LTD., Feltham, Middlesex.

125

Truck Fire Fighting Foam (Alvis Mk. 6A 6 x 6)
(Project State—In Service)

Description: This vehicle has been developed to meet an Air Ministry requirement for a highly mobile Fire Crash Tender capable of negotiating all types of terrain at high speeds, and dealing with fires in large aircraft. A unit capable of producing 9,000 gallons of foam in two minutes, dispersing from a monitor on the vehicle and two side hoses 60′ 0″ long, is installed together with a 16 gallon Chlorobromomethane unit provided with two 100′ hand lines. The body is insulated and heating facilities are provided to render the vehicle operational under a wide range of climatic conditions. A crew of six is carried and special equipment includes a power saw and rescue ladders, two-way radio and night operation lighting.

F.V. Specification Number: Chassis 9252. Body 9252. Equipment 9252.

Height: 10′ 0″ (*3·05 m.*).   Length: 18′ 0″ (*5·50 m.*).
Width: 8′ 3″ (*2·52 m.*).   Wheelbase: 10′ 0″ (*3·05 m.*).
Track: All Wheels 6′ 8½″ (*2·05 m.*).
Weight: Unladen 13,776 lb. (*6,249 kg.*).   Laden: 30,240 lb. (*13,717 kg.*).

PERFORMANCE DATA

Speed: average maximum:
Road 45 m.p.h. (*72·4 km./h.*).
C.C. 25 m.p.h. (*40·2 km./h.*).
Range of action at average maximum speed: 90 miles (*144 km.*).
Gross power weight ratio (b.h.p. per ton): 17·8.
Maximum tractive effort, low gear (lb. per ton): 1,290.
Maximum climbing ability: 1 in 2·2.
Maximum gradient for stop and restart: 1 in 3·2.

TECHNICAL DATA

Power Unit
Type: Rolls-Royce, B81, Mk. 8A, gasoline.
Displacement: 6,522 c.c. (398 cu. in.).
Gross B.H.P.: 238 at 4,000 r.p.m.
Nett torque: 322 lb. ft. at 2,250 r.p.m.
Speed limited to: 4,000 r.p.m.
Ignition type: Coil, 24 volt.

Fuel System
Type: Mechanical lift pump.
Type of fuel: Gasoline.
Air cleaner: Oil bath.
Fuel capacity: 27 gallons (*123 litres*).

Engine Lubrication
System: Dry sump.

Engine Cooling
System: Pressurised.

Wheels
Rims: WD divided disc light alloy.
Tyres: 14·00″ × 20″ pneumatic C.C.
Tyre Pump: Compressor, engine driven.
Chains: Can be fitted.

Transmission
Clutch: Fluid coupling.
Gearbox: Pre-selector 5-speed.
Transfer box: Forward and reverse and power take off.

Transmission—*continued*
Transfer box ratios: 2·43 : 1.
Propeller shafts: Muff couplings.
Axles: Articulating shafts.
Ratios: top 10·05 : 1, bottom 103·3 : 1.
Differentials: Central 4 star.

Brakes
Foot: Air-hydraulic drum.
Hand: Mechanical all wheels.

Steering
System: Recirculating ball, hydraulic assisted.
Turning circle: R.H. 50′ (*15·24 metres*). L.H. 50′ (*15·24 metres*).

Suspension
Front: Independent all wheels by double wishbone and torsion bar.
Rear: Independent all wheels by double wishbone and torsion bar.
Shock absorbers: Hydraulic telescopic.

Electrical Equipment
Generator: Single speed 16 amp.
Batteries: 2 12 volt 75 A.H.
Suppression: To F.V.R.D.E.
Specification 2051, Appendix DI, Schedule A.

MANUFACTURERS

Chassis:
Body: ⎱ ALVIS LTD., Coventry.

127

Truck Fire Fighting Foam
(Thornycroft Nubian Mk.VII 6 x 6)

(Project State—In Service)

Description: This vehicle has been developed for the Royal Air Force to meet the requirement for a high performance fire crash tender. The vehicle has a water tank capacity of 700 gallons (*3,188 litres*) and a foam tank capacity of 110 gallons (*5,005 litres*). The water pump and air blower are driven from the engine power take off and can produce foam through the high output monitor at 5,000 gallons per minute for 1·8 minutes with a throw of 95′ (*29 m.*). The vehicle is capable of good cross country performance and has a maximum road speed of 65 m.p.h. A crew of five can be carried in the cab.

Height: 10′ 4″ (*3·1 m.*).   Length: 23′ 10½″ (*7·28 m.*).
Width: 8′ 0″ (*2·84 m.*).   Wheelbase: 12′ 3″ (*3·74 m.*).
Track: Front 6′ 2″ (*1·88 m.*). Rear 6′ 3½″ (*1·91 m.*).
Weight: Laden 31,360 lb. (*14,220 kg.*).

PERFORMANCE DATA

Speed, average maximum:
Road 45 m.p.h. (*72·5 km.h.*).
    C.C. 18 m.p.h. (*29 km./h.*).
Range of action at average maximum speed: 100 miles (*161 km.*).
Gross power weight ratio (b.h.p. per ton): 16·75.
Maximum tractive effort, low gear (lb. per ton): 1,900.

TECHNICAL DATA

Power Unit
Type: Rolls-Royce, B81, Mk. 70K, gasoline.
Displacement: 6,522 c.c. (398 cu. in.).
Gross B.H.P.: 235 at 4,000 r.p.m.
Nett torque: 320 lb. ft. at 2,500 r.p.m.
Speed limited)to: 4,000 r.p.m.
Ignition type: Coil 24 volt.

Fuel System
Type: Lift pump.
Type of fuel: Gasoline.
Air cleaner: Oil bath.
Fuel capacity: 20 gallons (*91 litres*).

Engine Lubrication
System: Wet sump.

Engine Cooling
System: Pressurised.

Wheels
Rims: 10·00″ × 20″ divided.
Tyres: 14·00″ 20″ × C.C.
Tyre pump: Air pressure system.
Chains: Non-skid front, overall rear.

Transmission
Clutch: Twin dry plate.
Gearbox: 5-speed synchromesh and reverse.

Transmission—*continued*
Transfer box: 2-speed.
Transfer box ratios: 2·20 : 1 and 1 : 1.
Propeller shafts: Hardy Spicer.
Axles: Spiral bevel front, worm rear.
Ratios: Top 7·25 : 1, bottom 100 : 1.
Differentials: 3.

Brakes
Foot: Air assisted hydraulic.
Hand: Mechanical.
Warning device: Light.

Steering
System: Cam and roller, power assisted.
Turning circle: R.H. 75′ (*22·8 metres*). L.H. 75′ (*22·8 metres*).

Suspension
Front: Semi-elliptic leaf springs.
Rear: Semi-elliptic leaf springs.
Shock absorbers: Hydraulic, front only.

Towing Attachments
Type: Front, loops. Rear, loops.

Electrical Equipment.
Generator: 1,440 watts max. output.
Batteries: 24 volt 120 A.H.
Suppression: Screened ignition.

MANUFACTURERS

Chassis: TRANSPORT EQUIPMENT (THORNYCROFT) LTD., Basingstoke.
Body:
Equipment: } PYRENE CO. LTD., Brentford.

Truck Fire Fighting Foam
(Thornycroft Nubian Major 6 x 6)
(Project State—Under Development)

Description: This chassis and cab has been developed to form the basis of a high capacity airport fire crash tender with excellent off road performance. Many of the chassis units are similar to those on Exhibit No. 94. The equipment will include a Coventry Climax Mk. 6 fire pump having a discharge rate of 750 gallons per minute. The appliance will carry 1,250 gallons of water and 120 gallons of foam liquid. Fire fighting controls will be hydraulically operated from the cab and from an offside panel. A feature of the cab is a rear entry for the crew which affords speedy entry and exit.

Height: 10′ 4″ (*3·1 m.*) (without monitor assy.). Length: 25′ 3¾″ (*7·62 m.*).
Width: 8′ 2″ (*2·48 m.*). Wheelbase: 15′ 0″ (*4·57 m.*).
Track: Front 6′ 4⅝″ (*1·95 m.*). Rear 6′ 2″ (*1·88 m.*).
Weight: Unladen 21,448 lb. (*9,680 kg.*). Laden 41,500 lb. (*18,700 kg.*).

PERFORMANCE DATA

Speed, maximum:
 Road, exceeding 55 m.p.h. (*90 km./h.*).
Speed, average maximum:
 Road, 34 m.p.h. (*55 km./h.*).
 C.C. 15 m.p.h. (*24·1 km./h.*).
Range of action at average maximum speed: 240 miles (*386 km.*).
Gross power weight ratio (b.h.p. per ton): 16·2.
Maximum climbing ability: 1 in 3.
Maximum gradient for stop and restart: 1 in 4.

TECHNICAL DATA

Power Unit
Type: Cummins, V8–300, Diesel.
Displacement: 12,864 c.c. (785 cu. in.).
Gross B.H.P.: 288 at 3,000 r.p.m.
Nett torque: 558 lb. ft. at 2,100 r.p.m.
Governed speed: 3,000 r.p.m.
Ignition type: Compression.
Fuel System
Type: Cummins Pressure-Time fuel injection system.
Type of fuel: Diesel.
Air cleaner: Oil bath.
Fuel capacity: 30 gallons (*136 litres*).
Engine Lubrication
System: Wet sump.
Engine Cooling
System: Pressurised.
Wheels
Rims: Divided disc.
Tyres: 14·00″ × 20″ C.C. or 15·00″ × 20″ C.C.
Tyre Pump: Air brake compressor.
Transmission
Clutch: Fluid 18″ dia. (*457 mm.*).
Gearbox: 5-speed epicyclic 1 reverse.
Transfer box: 2-speeds.
Transfer box ratios: 1 : 1, 1·62 : 1.
Propeller shafts: Hardy Spicer.

Transmission—*continued*
Axles: Driven front and rear.
Ratios: Top, 7·9 : 1, bottom 93 : 1.
Differentials: Three.
Brakes
Foot: Air pressure dual system.
Hand: Mechanical multi-fuel.
Warning device: Light.
Steering
System: Cam and roller with power (hydraulic) assistance.
Turning circle: R.H. 77′ 3″ (*23·6 metres*). L.H. 77′ 9″ (*23·7 metres*), 14·00″ × 20″ tyres.
 R.H. 89′ (*27 metres*).
L.H. 92′ 6″ (*28 metres*), 15·00″ × 20″ tyres.
Suspension
Front: Semi-elliptic springs.
Rear: Semi-elliptic inverted springs.
Shock absorbers: Telescopic hydraulic dampers at front.
Electrical Equipment
Generator: 7″ a.c. 1,400 watts max. output.
Batteries: 24 volt 165 A/H.
Suppression: To F.V.R.D.E. Specification 2051, Appendix D1, Schedule B.

MANUFACTURERS

Chassis: Transport Equipment (Thornycroft) Ltd., Basingstoke.

Truck Tanker, Fuel, Servicing Aircraft
(1000 gallon Airportable Bedford 3 ton 4 x 2)

(Project State—In Service)

Description: This vehicle was designed and built to meet an Air Ministry requirement for a 1,000 gallons (*4,550 litres*) dual purpose refueller and in its unladen condition to be transportable in transport aircraft. The basic chassis is a 3-ton 4 × 2 TKFL Bedford and the tank is constructed of aluminium and three point mounted to the frame. The pump is driven from a power take-off and can deliver fuel at 150 gallons (*682·5 litres*) per minute for refuelling and 100 gallons (*455 litres*) per minute for self-loading. Defuelling from aircraft is at 50 gallons (*227·5 litres*) per minute.

Height: 8′ 3½″ (*2·52 m.*).
Length: 22′ 2″ (*6·75 m.*).
Width: 7′ 6″ (*2·28 m.*).
Wheelbase: 13′ 11″ (*4·24 m.*).
Track: Front 6′ 0¼″ (*1·83 m.*).   Rear 5′ 7⅛″ (*1·71 m.*).
Weight: Unladen 13,608 lb. (*6,130 kg.*).   Laden 21,900 lb. (*9,860 kg.*).

PERFORMANCE DATA

Speed, average maximum:
    Road 28 m.p.h. (*45 km./h.*).
    C.C.: 15 m.p.h. (*24·2 km./h.*).
Range of action at average maximum speed: 250 miles (*405 km.*).
Gross power weight ratio (b.h.p. per ton): 10·62.
Maximum tractive effort, low gear (lb. per ton): 750.
Maximum climbing ability: 1 in 3.
Maximum gradient for stop and restart: 1 in 4.

TECHNICAL DATA

Power Unit
Type: Bedford, 330 cu. in., Diesel.
Displacement: 5,418 c.c. (*330·6 cu. in.*).
Gross B.H.P.: 104 at 2,600 r.p.m.
Nett torque: 234 lb. ft. at 1,800 r.p.m.
Governed speed: 2,800 r.p.m.
Ignition type: Compression.

Fuel System
Type: Mechanical lift pump.
Type of fuel: Diesel.
Air cleaner: Oil bath.
Fuel capacity: 26 gallons (*118 litres*).

Engine Lubrication
System: Wet sump.

Engine Cooling
System: Pressurised.

Wheels
Rims: B6·00 × 20.
Tyres: 8·25″ × 20″ × 12 ply.
Chains: Non-skid rear only.

Transmission
Clutch: Single dry plate 13″ dia. (*330 mm.*).

Transmission—*continued*
Gearbox: 4-speed synchromesh and reverse.
Propeller shafts: Hardy Spicer.
Axle (rear): Fully floating spiral bevel.
Ratios: top 6·8 : 1, bottom 48 : 1.
Differentials: 1.

Brakes
Foot: Air/hydraulic.
Hand: Drum on transmission.
Warning device: Light.

Steering
System: Semi-irreversible worm and sector.
Turning circle: R.H. 55′ (*16·7 metres*). L.H. 55′ (*16·7 metres*).

Suspension
Front: Semi-elliptic springs.
Rear: Semi-elliptic springs.
Shock absorbers(Front): Telescopic hydraulic double acting.

Electrical Equipment
Generator: 12 volt 337 watts.
Batteries: 12 volt 185 A.H.

MANUFACTURERS

Chassis: VAUXHALL MOTORS LTD., Luton.
Equipment: ZWICKY LTD., Slough.

Truck Tanker, Fuel, Servicing Aircraft
(2,200 gallon Airportable AEC Mercury 4 x 2)
(Project State—In Service)

Description: This vehicle has been designed and built to meet an Air Ministry operational requirement and in its unladen condition is air transportable in the Argosy aircraft. The basic chassis is a Mercury 4×2 Mk. 2 (A.E.C.). The tank of 2,200 gallons (*10,000 litres*) capacity is constructed from aluminium alloys and is flexibly mounted to the frame at six points. The cab top and steering wheel are removable to facilitate entry into the aircraft. For refuelling under pressure, fuel can be delivered at 300 gallons (*1,365 litres*) per minute and for defuelling 70 gallons (*318 litres*) per minute minimum.

F.V. Specification Number: Chassis 9080.

Height: 6′ 2″ (*1·88 m.*).   Length: 30′ 0″ (*9·15 m.*).
Width: 8′ 1″ (*2·46 m.*).   Wheelbase: 17′ 3″ (*5·26 m.*).
Track: Front 6′ 4⅜″ (*1·94 m.*).   Rear: 5′ 11⅝″ (*1·82 m.*).
Weight: Unladen 14,000 lb. (*6,300 kg.*). Laden 31,400 *lb.* (*14,300 kg.*).

PERFORMANCE DATA

Speed, average maximum:
  Road 30 m.p.h. (*48·3 km./h.*).
Range of action at average maximum speed: 300 miles (*483 km.*).
Gross power weight ratio (b.h.p. per ton): laden 10.
Maximum tractive effort, low gear (lb. per ton): 555.
Maximum climbing ability: 1 in 6·4.
Maximum gradient for stop and restart: 1 in 6·4.

TECHNICAL DATA

Power Unit
Type: A.E.C., AV470, Diesel.
Displacement: 7,685 c.c. (470 cu. in.).
Gross B.H.P.: 138 at 2,200 r.p.m.
Nett torque: 338 lb. ft. at 1,000 r.p.m.
Governed speed: 2,200 r.p.m.
Ignition type: Compression.
Fuel System
Type: Lift pump.
Type of fuel: Diesel.
Air cleaner: Oil bath.
Fuel capacity: 40 gallons (*182 litres*).
Engine Lubrication
System: Wet sump.
Engine Cooling
System: Pressurised.
Wheels
Rims: Disc.
Tyres: 11·00″ × 20″ C.C.
Tyre pump: Air brake compressor.
Transmission
Clutch: Single plate 14″ (356 *mm.*).
Gearbox: 5-speed constant mesh, 1 reverse.

Transmission—*continued*
Transfer box: —
Transfer box ratios: —
Propeller shafts: Hardy Spicer.
Axle: Rear, fully floating single reduction.
Ratios: top 5·87 : 1, bottom 39 : 1.
Differentials: One.
Brakes
Foot: 2 line air pressure.
Hand: Mechanical on rear wheels only.
Warning device: Pressure gauge.
Steering
System: Worm and nut.
Turning Circle: R.H. 73′ 9″ (*22·5 metres*). L.H. 64′ 6″ (*19·65 metres*).
Suspension
Front: Semi-elliptic springs.
Rear: Semi-elliptic springs.
Shock Absorbers: Front only.
Electrical Equipment
Generator: 5″ dia. 24 volt.
Batteries: 94 amp./h. 24 volt.
Suppression: To F.V.R.D.E. Specification 2051, Appendix D1, Schedule B.

MANUFACTURERS

Chassis: A.E.C. Ltd., Southall, Middx.
Tank and Equipment: Zwicky Ltd., Slough.

Motor Coach, Large with Ambulance Role
(Bedford 4 x 2   39 Seat/16 Stretcher)
(Project State—Vehicles in Service)

Description: A 39 seat passenger coach built on a Bedford S.B3 chassis. The body is constructed so that it can readily be adapted to carry 16 stretchers for use as a temporary ambulance. A tropicalized version is also available having extra sliding windows but no heater.

F.V. Specification Number: Body 9687.

Height: 9′ 7″ (*2·92 m.*).   Length: 30′ 0″ (*9·14 m.*).
Width: 8′ 0″ (*2·44 m.*).   Wheelbase: 18′ 0″ (*5·49 m.*).
Track: Front 6′ 2½″ (*1·89 m.*).   Rear: (Mean) 5′ 9″ (*1·75 m.*).
Weight: Unladen 11,228 lb. (*5,093 kg.*). Laden: 18,500 lb. (*8,393 kg.*).

PERFORMANCE DATA

Speed, average maximum:
Road 42 m.p.h. (*67 km./h.*).
Range of action at average maximum speed: 180 miles (*288 km.*).
Gross power weight ratio (b.h.p. per ton): 16·2.

TECHNICAL DATA

Power Unit
Type: Bedford, 300 cu. in. gasoline.
Displacement: 4,927 c.c. (300 cu. in.).
Gross B.H.P. 130 at 3,200 r.p.m.
Nett torque: 222 lb. ft. at 1,200 r.p.m.
Governed speed: 3,200 r.p.m.
Ignition type: Coil, 12 volt.

Fuel System
Type: Lift pump.
Type of fuel: Gasoline.
Air cleaner: Oil bath.
Fuel capacity: 26 gallons (*118 litres*).

Engine Lubrication
System: Wet sump.

Engine Cooling
System: Pressurised.

Wheels
Rims: B 6·0″ × 20″. 8 stud 3 pce.
Tyres: 8·25″ × 20″ 12 ply.

Transmission
Clutch: 12″ single dry plate (*305 mm.*).
Gearbox: 4-speed wide ratio synchromesh, 1 reverse.

Transmission—*continued*
Propeller shafts: Hardy Spicer.
Axles: Fully floating Hypoid rear. I. beam front.
Ratios: top 5·83 : 1, bottom 41·18 : 1.
Differentials: One.

Brakes
Foot: Vacuum Servo assisted hydraulic with tandem piston master cylinder.
Hand: Mechanical on rear wheels.

Steering
System: Semi-irreversible worm and sector.
Turning circle: R.H. 64′ 6″ (*19·65 metres*). L.H. 64′ 6″ (*19·65 metres*).

Suspension
Front: Semi-elliptic.
Rear: Semi-elliptic.
Shock absorbers: Telescopic hydraulic front and rear.

Electrical Equipment
Generator: 500W 12 volt.
Batteries: 2 × 6V 129 A/H.
Suppression: To F.V.R.D.E.
Specification 2051, Appendix D1, Schedule B.

MANUFACTURERS

Chassis: VAUXHALL MOTORS.
Body: STRACHANS (SUCCESSORS) COACH-BUILDER, Hamble.

Equipment Radar Trailer Mounted S.A.G.W. A.A. No. 12 Mk. 1 (5 ton)

(Project State—In Service)

Description: This trailer has been designed to carry a height finding radar aerial. The centre section of the chassis consists of a welded tubular space frame while the rear section is of rivetted box section aluminium construction. The front suspension is by beam axle and semi-elliptic springs whilst at the rear independent coil spring wishbone type suspension is used. Suspension restraining gear is fitted at each wheel station to facilitate deployment.

F.V. Specification Number: Running Gear: 9274.

Height: 9′ 8″ (*2·95 m.*).   Length: 31′ 6½″ (*9·61 m.*) (including drawbar); 24′ 11″ (*7·60 m.*) (less drawbar).
Width: 8′ 8¾″ (*2·66 m.*).   Wheelbase: 16′ 0″ (*4·88 m.*).
Track: Front 7′ 4″ (*2·24 m.*).   Rear 7′ 3½″ (*2·22 m.*).
Weight: Laden 20,600 lb. (*9,344 kg.*).

TECHNICAL DATA

Wheels
Rims: B 8·00 × 15 3-piece.
Tyres: 10·00″ × 15″, 14 ply.

Brakes
Service: 2-line air/hydraulic.
Hand: Mechanical/hydraulic.

Steering
Type: Ackermann.

Turning circle: R.H. 61′ (*18·59 metres*). L.H. 61′ (*18·59 metres*).

Suspension
Front: Semi-elliptic.
Rear: Coil.
Shock absorbers: Double acting hydraulic telescopic type.

MANUFACTURERS

Chassis and Equipment: THE MARCONI Co. Ltd., Chelmsford, Essex.
Running Gear: RUBERY, OWEN & CO. LTD., Darlaston, Staffs.

Trailer Antenna SAGW A.A. No. 11 (5 ton)

(Project State—In Service)

Description: The chassis frame on this trailer is of welded steel construction. Independent suspension is fitted front and rear and consists of trailing box section wheel arms sprung by torsion bars.

F.V. Specification Number: Running Gear 9272.

Height: 11′ 10″ (*3·61 m.*). Length: 42′ 0½″ (*12·8 m.*) (including drawbar).
33′ 6″ (*10·2 m.*) (less drawbar).
Width: 8′ 9″ (*2·66 m.*).   Wheelbase: 15′ 6″ (*4·72 m.*).
Track: Front 7′ 4″ (*2·24 m.*).   Rear 7′ 4″ (*2·24 m.*).
Weight: Laden 18,930 lb. (*8,586 kg.*).

TECHNICAL DATA

Wheels
Rims: B 8·00 × 15- 3 piece.
Tyres: 10·00″ × 15″ 14-ply standard tread.

Brakes
Service: 2-line air/hydraulic.
Parking: Mechanical/hydraulic.

Steering
System: Ackermann.
Turning circle: R.H. 60′ (*18·3 metres*). L.H. 60′ (*18·3 metres*).

Suspension
Front: Torsion Bar.
Rear: Torsion Bar.
Shock absorbers: Double acting hydraulic lever type.

MANUFACTURERS

Running Gear: TASKERS OF ANDOVER (1932) LTD., Andover, Hants.
Chassis and Equipment: MARCONI CO. LTD., Chelmsford, Essex.
Special Equipment: To facilitate air or sea transportation hydraulic manually operated retraction gear is fitted to enable the vehicle running gear to be raised or lowered.

Equipment Radar, Trailer Mounted, S.A.G.W.A.A. No. 11 Mk. 1 (5 ton)

(Project State—In Service)

Description: This trailer consists of a light alloy double skin cabin of monocoque design with independent coil spring suspension front and rear. The front wheels are mounted on light alloy, parallel, leading arms and the rear on fabricated steel trailing arms. The vehicle can be lowered to the ground for deployment purposes by the use of mechanical jacks and retractable running gear.

F.V. Specification Number: Running Gear 9273.

Height: 7′ 9″ (*2·36 m.*).   Length: (including tow-bar) 26′ 5″ (*8·05 m.*).
Width: 9′ 0″ (*2·74 m.*).   Wheelbase: 12′ 10¾″ (*3·92 m.*).
Track: Front 7′ 7″ (*2·31 m.*).   Rear: 7′ 7″ (*2,31 m.*).
Weight: Laden 18,620 lb. (*8,445 kg.*).

TECHNICAL DATA

Wheels
Rims: B8·00″ × 15″ 3-piece.
Tyres: 10·00″ × 15″ 14 ply standard tread.

Brakes
Service: 2-line air/hydraulic.
Hand: Mechanical/hydraulic.

Steering
System: Ackermann.
Turning Circle: 60′ R.H. (*18·3 m.*).
60′ L.H. (*18·3 m.*).

Suspension
Front: Independent, coil spring.
Rear: Independent, coil spring.
Shock absorbers: Double acting hydraulic telescopic type.

MANUFACTURERS

Running Gear: TASKERS OF ANDOVER (1932) LTD., Andover, Hants.
Body: MICKLEOVER TRANSPORT LTD., Park Royal, London, N.W.10.
Equipment: THE MARCONI CO. LTD., Chelmsford, Essex.

Equipment Radar, Trailer Mounted, AA No. 10 Mk. 1, (7½ ton)

(Project State—In Service)

Description: This trailer has been designed to house and transport radar No. 10 Mk. 1. The body is of welded steel construction with rivetted aluminium panels externally and hardboard panels internally. Air conditioning is provided by sill-mounted air-conditioning units.

F.V. Specification Number: Chassis 9261. Body 9261.

Height: 9′ 9″ (*2·97 m.*).   Length: 20′ 6½″ (*6·26 m.*).
Width: 8′ 3½″ (*2·53 m.*).   Wheelbase: 10′ 6″ (*3·2 m.*).
Track: Front 6′ 7″ (*2·0 m.*).   Rear: 5′ 10″ (*1·78 m.*).
Weight: Laden 21,750 lb. (*9,860 kg.*).

TECHNICAL DATA

Wheels
Rims: B8·00″ × 15″.
Tyres: 10·00″ × 15″ standard tread, 14 ply.

Brakes
2-line air pressure on all wheels.

Service
Parking: Screw operated on rear wheels.

Steering
System: Ackermann type.
Turning circle: R.H. 21′ 11″ (*6·68 m.*). L.H. 19′ 6″ (*5·94 m.*).

Suspension
Front: Semi-elliptic springs.
Rear: Semi-elliptic springs.
Shock Absorbers: Telescopic hydraulic.

MANUFACTURERS

Chassis:
Body:
} RUBERY, OWEN & CO. LTD., Darlaston, Staffs.

Photographic Film Processing Hand Trailer Mounted (2 ton Airportable)
(Project State—In Service)

Description: This vehicle consists of a special house-type body mounted on to the standard 2-ton 4-wheel low loading trailer chassis F.V. 2504 Mk. 1 and its overall dimensions are such that it can be airported in the Beverley Aircraft. The body, which is fully insulated and air conditioned, is equipped as a dark room in which air film in width from 35 mm. to $9\frac{1}{2}''$ can be processed. Adequate provision is provided for water and chemical stowage.

F.V. Specification Number: Body 9700.

Height: 9′ 5·5″ (*2·95 m.*).   Length: 22′ 7″ (*6·88 m.*). including towbar.
Width: 8′ 0″ (*2·44 m.*).   Wheelbase: 12′ 0″ (*3·66 m.*).
Track: Front 6′ 2″ (*1·88 m.*).   Rear: 6′ 2″ (*1·88 m.*).
Weight: Laden 10,200 lb. (*4,610 kg.*).

TECHNICAL DATA

Wheels
Rims: 6·00″ × 16″.
Tyres: 9·00″ × 16″.

Brakes
Service: 2 line air pressure.
Parking: Mechanical on rear wheels.

Suspension
Front: ⎱
Rear: ⎰ Semi-elliptic.

Steering
System: Ackermann.

Jacking
4-screw type attached to chassis.

MANUFACTURERS

Chassis: TASKERS OF ANDOVER (1932) LTD., Andover, Hants.
RUBERY, OWEN CO. LTD., Darlaston, Staffs.
SENTINEL (SHREWSBURY) LTD., Shrewsbury, Shropshire.
Body: T. HARRINGTON & SONS LTD., Hove, Sussex.

Trailer Low Platform Earth Moving Ancillaries (2 ton)

(Project State—In Service)

Description: This trailer uses many components common to the 2 ton, 4 wheeled, FV.2505(D) trailer, Exhibit No. 71. It is designed to carry the ancillary and other equipment for use on the light Michigan and medium Gainsborough wheeled earthmoving tractors. It can be towed by either of the tractors or by a 3 ton G.S. vehicle.

F.V. Specification Number: Chassis 9319. Body 9319.

Height: Unladen *4′ 10″ (1·475 m.).*　Length: *25′ 1″ (7·65 m.).*
Width: 7′ 0″ (*2·14 m.*).　Wheelbase: 12′ 0″ (*3·66 m.*).
Track: Front 5′ 7″ (*1·7 m.*).　Rear: 5′ 7″ (*1·7 m.*).
Weight: Laden max. 10,250 lb. (*4,650 kg.*).

TECHNICAL DATA

Wheels
Rims: 6·50″H × 16″ divided 8 stud fixing type.
Tyres: 9·00″ × 16″ 10 ply.

Brakes
Service: 2-line air pressure.
Parking: Mechanical hand brake on rear wheels.

Steering
System: Ackermann.

Suspension
Front: Semi-elliptic springs.
Rear: Semi-elliptic springs.

Towing Attachments
Draught eye.

MANUFACTURERS

Chassis:
Body: } RUBERY, OWEN & CO. LTD., Darlington.

Trailer Flat Platform (2 ton)

(Project State—In Service)

Description: This is a general purpose flat platform variant of the F.V. 2505 series trailer. It is of 2 ton capacity and is normally towed behind a Bedford 3 ton 4 × 4 G.S. truck. It is capable of shallow fording to a depth of 30″ in fresh or sea water without preparation. A spare wheel and four stabilising jacks are fitted.

F.V. Specification Number: Chassis 9287.

Height: 2′ 6½″ (*0·75 m.*).   Length: 25′ 2″ (*7·65 m.*).
Width: 7′ 9″ (*2·36 m.*).   Wheelbase: 12′ 10″ (*3·66 m.*).
Track: Front 6′ 9″ (*2·06 m.*).   Rear: 6′ 9″ (*2·06 m.*).
Weight: Laden 11,620 lb. (*5,300 kg.*).

TECHNICAL DATA

Wheels
Rims: 6·50H″ × 16″ divided.
Tyres: 9·00 × 16″ 10 ply.

Brakes
Service: 2 air line pressure system.

Parking: Mechanical hand brake

on rear wheels only.

Suspension
Front: Semi-elliptic springs.
Rear: Semi-elliptic springs.

Towing Attachment
Type: Front, draught eye.

MANUFACTURERS

Chassis:
Body: } RUBERY, OWEN & CO. LTD.

Trailer Class 16 Airportable Bridge (1 ton)

(Project State—Under Development)

Description: This trailer is designed to carry sections of the class 16 airportable bridge. Welded steel construction is used throughout and independent trailing arm suspension is fitted using rubber springs. Each trailing wheel arm is retractable to assist in the loading and off loading of the bridge sections and this feature can also be used to reduce overall height for airporting. The suspension system is similar to that used on the ET.316 supply trailer FV.2411. Exhibit No. 73.

Height: Unladen 2′ 8″ (*0·81 m.*).   Length: 12′ 6″ (*3·8 m.*).
Width: 6′ 5″ (*1·95 m.*).   Track: 5′ 9″ (*1·75 m.*).
Weight: Laden approx. 3,000 lb. (*1,365 kg.*).

TECHNICAL DATA

Wheels
Rims: Well base 5·50″ × 16″.
Tyres: 7·50″ × 16″.

Brakes
Service: Over-run hydraulic.
Manoeuvering: Mechanical actuation on hydraulic brakes.

Brakes—*continued*
Parking: Mechanical separate on each wheel.

Suspension
Trailing arm with Aeon rubber springs.

Towing Attachments
Draught eye.

MANUFACTURERS

Chassis: PROTOTYPE GKN GROUP SERVICES LTD.

Trailer Supply SAGW. ET316 (1 ton)
(Project State—Under Development)

Description: This is a prototype of a trailer designed to carry packaged missiles for ET.316 System. It will normally be towed by the L.W.B. Landrover ¾ ton truck. The frame is a welded steel structure. The suspension system is by trailing arms supported on rubber springs and is similar to that being developed for the Airportable Bridge Trailer FV.2420 Exhibit No. 72. The facility exists for retracting the wheels to ease loading operation or for reducing overall height for airporting if this is necessary.

Height: 3′ 10½″ (*1·18 m.*).   Length: 11′ 6″ (*3.50 m.*).
Width: 5′ 5″ (*1·65 m.*).   Track: 4′ 8½″ (*1.43 m.*).
Weight: Laden Approx. 3,000 lb. (*1,362 kg.*).

TECHNICAL DATA

Wheels
Rims: Well base 5·50 × 16.
Tyres: 7·50 × 16.
Brakes
Service: Mechanical, over-run.

Parking: Mechanical, hand operated.
Suspension
Trailing arm with Aeon rubber springs.

154

MANUFACTURERS

GKN GROUP SERVICES LTD.

F.V. 2401(R)

Generating Set Diesel Engine
10 KVA Trailer Mounted (1 ton)
(Project State—In Service)

Description: This is the basic 1-ton, 2-wheeled, chassis F.V. 2401(A) Exhibit No. 75 with flat platform on which is installed the 10 kVA 415/240 volt 50 c/s 3 phase generator set.

F.V. Specification Number: Chassis 9054. Body 9305.

Height: 7′ 0″ (*2·13 m.*).   Length: 11′ 10″ (*3·33 m.*).
Width: 6′ 10″ (*2·08 m.*).   Track: 5′ 7″ (*1·7 m.*).
Weight: Laden 3,900 lb. (*1,775 kg.*).

TECHNICAL DATA

Wheels
Rims: 6·50 × 16 divided wheel.
Tyres: 9·00 × 16″.

Brakes
Service: Over-run.
Parking: Mechanical hand brake.
Suspension
Semi-elliptic.

MANUFACTURERS

Chassis:
- J. SANKEY & SONS LTD.
- J. BROCKHOUSE LTD.
- RUBERY, OWEN & CO. LTD.

Equipment: AUTO DIESEL LTD.

Trailer Cargo (1 Ton)

(Project State—In Service)

Description: This trailer is of pressed-steel, welded-frame construction with semi-elliptic suspension mounted on a single tubular axle. Braking on both wheels is actuated by an over-run mechanism from the draught eye. A cargo body with a hardwood floor and drop tailboard is fitted.

F.V. Specification Number: Chassis 9054.

Height: 4′ 0″ (*1·22 m.*).　Length: 11′ 3″ (*3·15 m.*).
Width: 6′ 10″ (*2·08 m.*).　Track: 5′ 7″ (*1·71 m.*).
Weight: Laden 3,920 lb. (1,780 *kg.*).

TECHNICAL DATA

Wheels
Rims: 6·50″ × 16″ divided wheel.
Tyres: 9·00″ × 16″.

Brakes
Service: Over-run mechanical.
Parking: Mechanical connection

Brakes—*continued*
to over-run.

Suspension
Semi-elliptic springs.

Towing Attachments
Type: Draught eye.

MANUFACTURERS

Chassis: J. SANKEY & SONS LTD.
Body: RUBERY, OWEN & CO. LTD.

ALTERNATIVE ROLES

The basic trailer is used for mounting numerous equipment such as generators, water tank and air cooling plants.

Air Conditioner Trailer Mounted
(No. 54 Mk. 2, 1 ton)
(Project State—In Service)

Description: The air conditioner No. 54 Mk. 2 is mounted on a 1-ton (Series F.V. 2400) trailer. It has a cooling capacity of 30,000 B.t.u./hr. in an air temperature of 120°F. with an air delivery of 1,600 c.f.m. It is automatically controlled from thermostats mounted in the conditioned vehicle. The cooling units are four sealed system Air Conditioners No. 52H Mk. 2 with booster fans. The trailer is air portable in current Service aircraft. The electrical requirement is 415 volts, 3 phase, 50 c.p.s.

F.V. Specification Number: Chassis 9054.

Height: 7′ 8″ (*2·34 m.*).   Length: 11′ 3″ (*3·43 m.*).
Width: 6′ 10″ (*2·08 m.*).   Track: 5′ 7″ (*1·7 m.*).
Weight: Laden 3,920 lb. (*1,780 kg.*).

TECHNICAL DATA

Wheels
Rims: W.D. divided wheel.
Tyres: 9·00″ × 20″.

Brakes
Service: Over-run mechanical.
Parking: Mechanical connection to

Brakes—*continued*
over-run.

Suspension
Front: Semi-elliptic springs.

Towing Attachments
Type: Front, draught eye.

MANUFACTURERS

Chassis: J. Sankey & Sons Ltd.
               J. Brockhouse Ltd.
Body: ⎫
Equipment: ⎬ Temperature Ltd.
               ⎭

Water Purification Unit, Trailer Mounted
(1000 GPH ¾ ton)
(Project State—In Service)

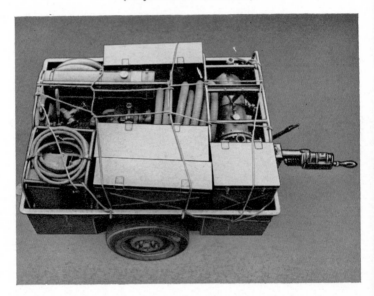

Description: This 2-wheeled ½ ton trailer is of pressed steel welded frame construction with semi-elliptic suspension mounted on a single tubular axle. Braking on both wheels is actuated by an over-run mechanism from the draught eye. The drawbar is reversible to suit varying heights of prime mover. For future production the equipment would be mounted on the chassis of Trailer F.V. 2361 Exhibit No. 6.

An all steel body of water-tight construction is installed with a water purification plant capable of an average output of 1,000 gph. of filtered and sterilized water against a static head of 80 ft.

F.V. Specification Number: Chassis/Body 9175.

Height 4′ 1″ (*1·24 m.*).   Length: 9′ 5″ (*2·87 m.*).
Width: 4′ 7″ (*1·4 m.*).

Track: 3′ 11½″ (*1·21 m.*).
Weight: Laden 2,018 lb. (*917 kg.*).

TECHNICAL DATA

Wheels
Rims: W.D. divided type.
Tyres: 6·00″ × 16″.

Brakes
Service: Over-run mechanical.

Parking: Mechanical connection
to service brake.

Suspension
Sem-elliptic springs.

MANUFACTURERS

Chassis: { J. SANKEY & SONS LTD.
{ J. BROCKHOUSE & CO. LTD.
Body: J. BROCKHOUSE & CO. LTD.

Welding Set Lightweight Trailer Mounted
($\frac{3}{4}$ ton)
(Project State—Under Development)

Description: This is a basic $\frac{3}{4}$ ton 2-wheeled trailer F.V. 2361 fitted
with a lightweight welding set. The trailer is of welded steel construction
and is fitted with stabilising jacks. The welding set is powered by a
Deutz 2-cylinder type F2L310, compression ignition engine rated at
18 b.p.h. at 3,000 r.p.m. The open circuit range is 15–35 volts D.C.
and a current of 200 amps is available on a 75% duty cycle. Ferrous
and non-ferrous metals can be welded using an M.I.G. shielded arc
gun employing a gas shield of either Argon or carbon dioxide.

F.V. Specification Number: Chassis 9307. Body 9307.

Height: 5′ 6″ (*1·675 m.*). Length: 9′ 7″ (*2·92 m.*).
Width: 4′ 8″ (*1·425 m.*).   Track: 3′ 11″ (*1·2 m.*).
Weight: Laden 2,352 lb. (*1,070 kg.*).

TECHNICAL DATA

Wheels
Rims: 4·50″E × 16″—5 stud fixing.
Tyres: 6·50″ × 16″.

Brakes
Service: Over-run mechanical.
Parking: Mechanical connection to over-run.

Suspension
Front: Semi-elliptic springs and Aeon rubber.
Shock absorbers: Telescopic hydraulic.

Towing Attachment
Front: Draught eye.

MANUFACTURERS

Chassis: ⎫
Body: ⎬ PRESSED STEEL CO. LTD.
Equipment: MUREX OR BRITISH OXYGEN CO. LTD.

Scout Car Liaison Mk. 1/1
(Daimler Ferret 4 x 4)

(Project State—In Service)

Description: This vehicle carries a crew of two or three and is used by all arms of the Service for liaison and reconnaissance duties, particularly in forward areas. It has an open top and mounts a ·303″ Bren gun on a pintle. Hull and superstructure are of welded armour plate and sealed for wading to a depth of 3′ 0″ without preparation.

F.V. Specification Number: Chassis 9235.

Height: 4′ 9″ (*1·45 m.*).   Length: 12′ 7″ (*3·84 m.*).
Width: 6′ 3″ (*1·91 m.*).   Wheelbase: 7′ 6″ (*2·29 m.*).
Track: Front 5′ 1″ (*1·58 m.*).   Rear 5′ 1″ (*1·58 m.*).
Weight: Basic 7,728 lb. (*3,510 kg.*).   Battle 9,296 lb. (*4,217 kg.*).

PERFORMANCE DATA

Speed, average maximum:
    Road 45 m.p.h. (*72 km./h.*).
    C.C. 25 m.p.h. (*40 km./h.*).
Range of action at average maximum speed: 190 miles (*305 km.*).
Gross power weight ratio (b.h.p. per ton): 31·1.
Maximum tractive effort, low gear (lb. per ton): 1,310.
Maximum climbing ability: 1 in 2·2.
Maximum gradient for stop and restart: 1 in 3·2.

TECHNICAL DATA

Power Unit
Type: Rolls-Royce, B60, Mk. 6A, gasoline.
Displacement: 4,260 c.c. (260 cu. in.).
Gross B.H.P.: 129 at 3,750 r.p.m.
Nett torque: 195 lb. ft. at 2,000 r.p.m.
Speed limited to: 3,750 r.p.m.
Ignition type: Coil, 24 volt.

Fuel System
Type: Mechanical pump.
Type of fuel: Gasoline.
Air cleaner: F.V. design oil bath.
Fuel capacity: 21 gallons (*96 litres*).

Engine Lubrication
System: Dry sump.

Engine Cooling
System: Pressurised.

Wheels
Rims: W.D. divided alloy.
Tyres: 9.00 × 16 R.F.
Tyre pump: Foot.
Chains: Can be fitted. Sand channels provided.

Transmission
Clutch: 13″ fluid coupling.
Gearbox: Pre-selector, 5-speed.

Transmission—*continued*
Transfer box: Differential and forward and reverse.
Transfer box ratios: 1·35 : 1.
Propeller shafts: Hardy Spicer.
Axles: Articulating shafts.
Ratios: top: 6·22 : 1, bottom: 37·58 : 1.
Differentials: Across vehicle.

Brakes
Foot: Hydraulic, vacuum servo drum.
Hand: Mechanical on all four wheels.

Steering
System: Recirculating ball.
Turning circle: R.H. 38′ (*11·58 metres*). L.H. 38′ (*11·58 metres*).

Suspension
Front: ⎱ Independent, double wish-
Rear: ⎰ bone, coil spring.
Shock absorbers: Hydraulic telescopic.

Electrical Equipment
Generator: 2-speed 25 amp.
Batteries: Two 12 volt 60 amp/h.
Suppression: To F.V.R.D.E. Spec. 2051 Appendix D1 Schedule B.

MANUFACTURERS

DAIMLER CO. LTD., Coventry.

F.V. 701(J)

Scout Car Floating Mk.1/1
(Daimler Ferret 4 x 4)
(Project State—Undergoing User Trials)

Description: This vehicle is identical to Exhibit No. 79 but is shown fitted with a floatation screen to enable the vehicle to cross water obstacles. The installation comprises a completely new wing line right round the vehicle, on which a screen of the camera bellows type is mounted. New watertight stowage lockers are provided. The screen can be very quickly raised or lowered, and transparent vision slots are provided in the front to enable the vehicle to be driven easily on land and in the water. Propulsion is by the road wheels only. This system may be applied to all of the Ferret series.

F.V. Specification Number: Chassis 9235.

Height: 4′ 9″ (*1·45 m.*).   Length: 13′ 5″ (*4·1 m.*).
Width: 6′ 2″ (*1·88 m.*).   Wheelbase: 7′ 6″ (*2·29 m.*).
Track: 5′ 1″ (*1·58 m.*).
Weight: Unladen 8,000 lb. (*3,640 kg.*).   Laden 9,568 lb. (*4,350 kg.*).

PERFORMANCE DATA

Speed, average maximum:
 Road 45 m.p.h. (*72·42 km./h.*).
 C.C. 25 m.p.h. (*40·23 km./h.*).
Range of action at average maximum speed: 190 miles (*305 km.*).
Gross power weight ratio (b.h.p. per ton): *30·2.*
Maximum tractive effort, low gear (lb. per ton): *1,280.*
Maximum climbing ability: 1 in 2·2.
Maximum gradient for stop and restart: 1 in 3·2.

TECHNICAL DATA

Power Unit
Type: Rolls-Royce, B60, Mk. 6A, gasoline.
Displacement: 4,260 c.c. (260 cu. in.).
Gross B.H.P.: 129 at 3,750 r.p.m.
Nett torque: 195 lb. ft. at 2,000 r.p.m.
Speed limited to: 3,750 r.p.m.
Ignition type: Coil, 24 volt.

Fuel System
Type: Mechanical pump.
Type of fuel: Gasoline.
Air cleaner: F.V. design oil bath.
Fuel capacity: 21 gallons (*96 litres*).

Engine Lubrication
System: Dry sump.

Engine Cooling
System: Pressurised.

Wheels
Rims: W.D. divided alloy.
Tyres: 9·00″ × 16″ R.F.
Tyre pump: Foot.
Chains: Can be fitted. Sand channels may be carried.

Transmission
Clutch: 13″ fluid coupling.
Gearbox: Pre-selector 5 speed.

Transmission—*continued*
Transfer box: Differential and forward and reverse.
Transfer box ratios: 1·35 : 1.
Propeller shafts: Hardy Spicer.
Axles: Articulating shafts.
Ratios: Top 6·22:1. Bottom 37·58:1.
Differentials: Across vehicle.

Brakes
Foot: Hydraulic, vacuum servo drum.
Hand: Mechanical on all four wheels.

Steering
System: Recirculating ball.
Turning circle: R.H. 38′ (*11·58 metres*). L.H. 38′ (*11·58 metres*).

Suspension
Front: ⎫ Independent double wish-
Rear: ⎭ bone coil spring all wheels.
Shock absorbers: Hydraulic telescopic.

Electrical Equipment
Generator: 2-speed 25 amp.
Batteries: 2 × 12 volt 60 amp/h.
Suppression: To F.V.R.D.E. Spec. 2051 Appendix D1 Schedule B.

MANUFACTURERS

Vehicle: Daimler Co. Ltd., Coventry.
Floatation Screen: Garner Motors, Sunbury.

Scout Car L.V.R. Mk.1/2 (Daimler Ferret 4 x 4)

(Project State—In Service)

Description: This vehicle carries a crew of three and is used by the infantry as a light liaison vehicle in forward areas. It has an armoured roof fitted with a hatch and mounts a ·303″ Bren gun on a pintle. Hull and superstructure are of welded armour plate and sealed for wading to a depth of 3′ 0″ without preparation.

Height: 5′ 5″ (*1·65 m.*).   Length: 12′ 7″ (*3·84 m.*).
Width: 6′ 3″ (*1·91 m.*).   Wheelbase: 7′ 6″ (*2·29 m.*).
Track: Front 5′ 1″ (*1·55 m.*).   Rear: 5′ 1″ (*1·55 m.*).
Weight: Unladen 8,064 lb. (*3,657 kg.*).   Laden 9,632 lb. (*4,369 kg.*).

PERFORMANCE DATA

Speed, average maximum:
    Road 45 m.p.h. (*72 km./h.*).   C.C. 25 m.p.h. (*40 km./h.*).
Range of action at average maximum speed: 190 miles (*306 km.*).
Gross power weight ratio (b.h.p. per ton): 30.

Maximum Tractive Effort, low gear (lb. per ton): 1,270.
Maximum climbing ability: 1 in 2·2.
Maximum gradient for stop and restart: 1 in 3·2.

TECHNICAL DATA

Power Unit
Type: Rolls-Royce B60, Mk. 6A, gasoline.
Displacement: 4,260 c.c. (260 cu. in.).
Gross B.H.P.: 129 at 3,750 r.p.m.
Nett torque: 195 lb. ft. at 2,000 r.p.m.
Speed limited to: 3,750 r.p.m.
Ignition type: Coil, 24 volt.

Fuel System
Type: Mechanical pump.
Type of fuel: Gasoline.
Air cleaner: F.V. design oil bath.
Fuel capacity: 21 gallons (96 litres).

Engine Lubrication
System: Dry sump.

Engine Cooling
System: Pressurised.

Wheels
Rims: W.D. divided alloy.
Tyres: 9·00″ × 16″ R.F.
Tyre pump: Foot.
Chains: Can be fitted. Sand channels provided.

Transmission
Clutch: 13″ fluid coupling.
Gearbox: Pre-selector, 5-speed.
Transfer box: Differential and forward and reverse.

Transmission—*continued*
Transfer box ratios: 1·35 : 1.
Propeller shafts: Hardy Spicer.
Axles: Articulating shafts.
Ratios: Top 6·22 : 1, bottom 37·58 : 1.
Differentials: Across vehicle.

Brakes
Foot: Hydraulic, vacuum servo, drum.
Hand: Mechanical on all four wheels.

Steering
System: Recirculating ball.
Turning circle: R.H. 38′ (*11·58 metres*). L.H. 38′ (*11·58 metres*).

Suspension
Front: Independent, double wishbone, coil spring.
Rear: Independent, double wishbone, coil spring.
Shock absorbers: Hydraulic telescopic.

Electrical Equipment
Generator: 2-speed 25 amp.
Batteries: 2 12 volt 60 amp./h.
Suppression: To F.V.R.D.E. Specification 2051, Appendix D1, Schedule B.

MANUFACTURERS

DAIMLER CO. LTD., Coventry.

ALTERNATIVE ROLES

1. Light reconnaissance infantry.

F.V. 701(H)

Scout Car Reconnaissance Mk. 2/3
(Daimler Ferret 4 x 4)

(Project State—In Service)

Description: This vehicle is basically similar to the Mk. 1 liaison Ferret but has a small turret fitted over the open top. The turret had a ·30″ Browning MG having an elevation of 45° and a depression of 15°. The hull and turret are of welded armour plate sealed for wading to a depth of 3′ 0″ without preparation. A crew of two is carried.

F.V. Specification Number: Chassis 9235.

Height: 6′ 2″ (*1·88 m.*).   Length: 12′ 7″ (*3·84 m.*).
Width: 6′ 3″ (*1·91 m.*).   Wheelbase: 7′ 6″ (*2·87 m.*).
Track: Front 5′ 1″ (*1·55 m.*).   Rear: 5′ 1″ (*1·55 m.*).
Weight: Unladen 8,120 lb. (*3,684 kg.*).   Laden 9,688 lb. (*4·395 kg.*).

PERFORMANCE DATA

Speed, average maximum:
    Road 45 m.p.h. (*72 km./h.*).
    C.C. 25 m.p.h. (*40 km./h.*).
Range of action at average maximum speed: 190 miles (*306 km.*).
Gross power weight ratio (b.h.p. per ton): 29·8.
Maximum tractive effort, low gear (lb. per ton): 1,260.
Maximum climbing ability: 1 in 2·2.
Maximum gradient for Stop and restart: 1 in 3·2.

TECHNICAL DATA

Power Unit
Type: Rolls-Royce B60 Mk. 6A gasoline.
Displacement: 4,260 c.c. (260 cu. in.).
Gross B.H.P.: 129 at 3,750 r.p.m.
Nett torque: 195 lb. ft. at 2,000 r.p.m.
Speed limited to: 3,750 r.p.m.
Ignition type: Coil 24 volt.

Fuel System
Type: Mechanical pump.
Type of fuel: Gasoline.
Air cleaner: F.V. design oil bath.
Fuel capacity: 21 gallons (*96 litres*).

Engine Lubrication
System: Dry sump.

Engine Cooling
System: Pressurised.

Wheels
Rims: W.D. divided alloy.
Tyres: 9·00 × 16 R.F.
Tyre pump: Foot.
Chains: Can be fitted. Sand channels provided.

Transmission
Clutch: 13″ fluid coupling.
Gearbox: Pre-selector, 5-speed.

Transmission—*continued*
Transfer box: Differential and forward and reverse.
Transfer box ratios: 1·35 : 1.
Propeller shafts: Hardy Spicer.
Axles: Articulating shafts.
Ratios: Top: 6·22 : 1, bottom 37·58 : 1.
Differentials: Across vehicle.

Brakes
Foot: Hydraulic, vacuum servo, drum.
Hand: Mechanical all four wheels.

Steering
System: Recirculating ball.
Turning circle: R.H. 38′ (*11·58 metres*). L.H. 38′ (*11·58 metres*).

Suspension
Front: ⎫ Independent, double wish-
Rear: ⎭ bone, coil spring.
Shock absorbers: Hydraulic telescopic.

Electrical Equipment
Generator: 2-speed 25 amp.
Batteries: Two 12 volt 60 amp/h.
Suppression: To F.V.R.D.E. Spec. 2051 Appendix D1, Schedule B.

MANUFACTURERS

DAIMLER CO. LTD., Coventry.

Scout Car Reconnaissance /G.W. Mk. 2 /6
(Daimler Ferret 4 x 4)
(Project State—In Service)

Description: This vehicle carries a crew of two and is used with armoured formations for reconnaissance purposes. The main armament is a ·30″ Browning having an elevation of 45° and a depression of 15°. The vehicle is adapted to carry four Vigilant, wire guided, anti-tank missiles. Two missiles are mounted on a common elevating mechanism on the turret sides in a ready to fire position. The remaining two are stowed alongside the hull in place of the spare wheel. The missiles can be controlled by the commander from inside the turret or from a separated position by using a combined sight/controller and separation cable.

F.V. Specification Number: Chassis/Body 9235. Equipment 9312.

Height: 6′ 2″ (*1·88 m.*).   Length: 12′ 7″ (*3·84 m.*).
Width: 6′ 3″ (*1·91 m.*).   Wheelbase: 7′ 6″ (*2·87 m.*).
Track: Front 5′ 1″ (*1·55 m.*). Rear: 5′ 1″ (*1·55 m.*).
Weight: Unladen 8,120 lb. (*3,684 kg.*).   Laden 9,988 lb. (*4,560 kg.*).

PERFORMANCE DATA

Speed, average maximum:
Road 45 m.p.h. (*72 km./h.*).
C.C. 25 m.p.h. (*40 km./h.*).
Range of action at average maximum speed: 190 miles (*306 km.*).
Gross power weight ratio: (b.h.p. per ton): 29.
Maximum tractive effort, low gear (lb. per ton): 1,230.
Maximum climbing ability: 1 in 2·2.
Maximum gradient for stop and restart: 1 in 3·2.

TECHNICAL DATA

Power Unit
Type: Rolls-Royce, B60 Mk. 6A, gasoline.
Displacement: 4,260 c.c. (260 cu. in.).
Gross B.H.P.: 129 at 3,750 r.p.m.
Nett torque: 195 at 2,000 r.p.m.
Speed limited to: 3,750 r.p.m.
Ignition type: Coil, 24 volt.

Fuel System
Type: Mechanical lift pump.
Type of Fuel: Gasoline.
Air cleaner: F.V. design oil bath.
Fuel capacity: 21 gallons (*96 litres*).

Engine Lubrication
System: Dry sump.

Engine Cooling
System: Pressurised.

Wheels
Rims: W.D. divided light alloy.
Tyres: 9·00″ × 16″ RF
Tyre pump: Foot.
Chains: Can be fitted, sand channels provided.

Transmission
Clutch: 13″ fluid coupling.
Gearbox: Pre selector, 5-speed.
Transfer box: Forward and reverse.

Transmission—*continued*
Transfer box ratios: 1·347: 1.
Propeller shafts: Hardy Spicer.
Axles: Articulating shafts.
Ratios: Top 6·22 : 1, bottom 37·58 : 1.
Differentials: One central.

Brakes
Foot: Hydraulic, vacuum servo, drum.
Hand: Mechanical all four wheels.

Steering
System: Recirculating ball.
Turning circle: R.H. 38′ (*11·58 metres*). L.H. 38′ (*11·58 metres*).

Suspension
Front: Independent, double wishbone, coil spring.
Rear: Independent, double wishbone, coil spring.
Shock absorbers: Hydraulic telescopic.

Electrical Equipment
Generator: 2-speed 25 amp.
Batteries: 2 12 volt 60 amp./h.
Suppression: To F.V.R.D.E. Specification 2051, Appendix D1, Schedule B.

MANUFACTURERS

DAIMLER CO. LTD., Coventry.

ALTERNATIVE ROLES

1. Reconnaissance.
2. Anti-tank.

Scout Car Reconnaissance Mk.4
(Daimler Ferret 4 x 4 Big Wheeled)
(Project State—Design and Development)

Description: This vehicle is an improved version of the Mk. 2 reconnaissance Ferret. The modifications made are automotive and consist of stronger suspension units, disc brakes, and larger wheels and tyres, to give an increased load capacity and better mobility. The wings and stowage bins have been designed to accept a floatation screen to enable the vehicle to swim in inland waterways. The road wheels provide water propulsion. The number of servicing points have been reduced in order to relieve the maintenance work load. Hull and turret are of welded armour plate. A crew of two is carried.

Height: 6′ 8″ (*2·03 m.*).   Length: 13′ 0″ (*3·96 m.*).
Width: 7′ 0″ (*2·13 m.*).   Wheelbase: 7′ 6″ (*2·29 m.*).
Track: Front 5′ 9″ (*1·75 m.*).   Rear 5′ 9″ (*1·75 m.*).
Weight: Unladen 10,500 lb. (*4,725 kg.*) (est.).   Laden 12,000 lb. (*5,400 kg.*).

PERFORMANCE DATA

Speed, average maximum:
    Road 40 m.p.h. (*64 km./h.*).
    C.C. 25 m.p.h. (*40 km./h.*).
Range of action at average maximum speed: 190 (*306 km.*).
Gross power weight ratio (b.h.p. per ton): 24·1.
Maximum tractive effort, low gear (lb. per ton): 1,240.
Maximum climbing ability: 1 in 2·2.
Maximum gradient for stop and restart: 1 in 3·2.

TECHNICAL DATA

Power Unit
Type: Rolls-Royce, B60, Mk. 6A, gasoline.
Displacement: 4,260 c.c. (260 cu. in.).
Gross B.H.P.: 129 at 3,750 r.p.m.
Nett torque: 195 lb. ft. at 2,000 r.p.m.
Speed limited to: 3,750 r.p.m.
Ignition Type: Coil, 24 volt.

Fuel System
Type: Mechanical pump.
Type of fuel: Gasoline.
Air cleaner: F.V. design oil bath.
Fuel capacity: 21 gallons (96 litres).

Engine Lubrication
System: Dry sump.

Engine Cooling
System: Pressurised.

Wheels
Rims: W.D. divided alloy.
Tyres: 11·00″ × 20″ RF
Tyre pump: Foot.
Chains: Can be fitted. Sand channels part of equipment.

Transmission
Clutch: 13″ fluid coupling.
Gearbox: Pre-selective 5-speed.
Transfer box: Differential and forward and reverse.

Transmission—*continued*
Propeller shafts: Hardy Spicer.
Axles: Articulating shafts.
Ratios: Top 9·08 : 1, bottom 54·8 : 1.
Differentials: Across vehicle.

Brakes
Foot: Hydraulic, vacuum servo 15″ disc.
Hand: Contracting band on front bevel box input.

Steering
System: Recirculating ball.
Turning circle: R.H. 38′ (*11·58 metres*). L.H. 38′ (*11·58 metres*).

Suspension
Front: Independent, double wishbone, coil spring.
Rear: Independent, double wishbone, coil spring.
Shock absorbers: Hydraulic telescopic.

Electrical Equipment
Generator: 2-speed 25 amp.
Batteries: 2 12 volt 60 amp./h.
Suppression: To F.V.R.D.E. Specification 2051, Appendix D1, Schedule B.

MANUFACTURERS

DAIMLER CO. LTD., Coventry.

ALTERNATIVE ROLES

Anti-tank.

Scout Car Reconnaissance/GW Mk. 5
(Daimler Ferret 4 x 4 Big Wheeled)

Description: This vehicle carries a crew of two and is used with armoured formations for reconnaissance purposes. In addition to a machine gun the vehicle carries six Swingfire anti tank guided missiles under armour. Four of these missiles are mounted in the turret, being elevated to fire, the other two being stowed on the hull. The Commander can control the missiles from the turret or from a remote position by using a combined sight/controller and a separation cable.

The vehicle performance and technical data is similar to Exhibit No. 84.

MANUFACTURER

Vehicle: DAIMLER CO. LTD.
Guided Weapon System: BRITISH AIRCRAFT CORPORATION.

Carrier Personnel Wheeled A.P.C. Mk.2
(Alvis Saracen 6 x 6)

(Project State—In Service)

Description: This vehicle is a carrier for personnel in Armoured and Armoured Car Regiments and in Divisional Engineer Units. The vehicle is capable of rapid conversion to a load carrier and a navigational vehicle. As an A.P.C. it carries a total of twelve men including driver and commander. Hull and turret are of welded armour plate sealed for wading to a depth of 3' 6" without preparation. A ·30" machine gun is mounted in the turret. A mounting ring is also provided for a Bren ·303" machine gun for use against aircraft.

F.V. Specification Number: Chassis 9125. Body 9125. Equipment 9125.

Height: 8' 0" (*2·44 m.*).   Length: 15' 11" (*4·85 m.*).
Width: 8' 3" (*2·52 m.*).   Wheelbase: 10' 0" (*3·05 m.*).
Track: all wheels 6' 8" (*2·03 m.*).
Weight: Unladen 19,040 lb. (*8,640 kg.*).   Laden 22,400 lb. (*10,170 kg.*).

PERFORMANCE DATA

Speed, average maximum:
    Road 35 m.p.h. (*56 km./h.*).
    C.C. 20 m.p.h. (*32 km./h.*).
Range of action at average maximum speed: 250 miles (*400 km.*).
Gross power weight ratio (b.h.p. per ton): 17·1.
Maximum tractive effort, low gear (lb. per ton): 1,595.
Maximum climbing ability: 1 in 2·2.
Maximum gradient for stop and restart: 1 in 3·2.

TECHNICAL DATA

Power Unit
Type: Rolls-Royce, B80, Mk. 6A, gasoline.
Displacement: 5,670 c.c. (346 cu. in.).
Gross B.H.P.: 170 at 3,750 r.p.m.
Nett torque: 260 lb. ft. at 2,000 r.p.m.
Speed limited to: 3,750 r.p.m.
Ignition type: Coil, 24 volt.
Fuel System
Type: Mechanical lift pump.
Type of fuel: Gasoline.
Air cleaner: F.V. design oil bath.
Fuel capacity: 44 gallons (*200 litres*).
Engine Lubrication
System: Dry sump.
Engine Cooling
System: Pressurised.
Wheels
Rims: W.D. pattern light alloy divided disc.
Tyres: 12·00″ × 20″ R.F.
Tyre Pump: Engine compressor.
Chains: Can be fitted.
Transmission
Clutch: Fluid coupling.
Gearbox: Pre-selector 5-speed.
Transfer box: Forward and reverse.
Transfer box ratios: 3·13 : 1.

Transmission—*continued*
Propeller shafts: Muff couplings.
Axles: Articulating shafts.
Ratios: Top 10·05 : 1, bottom 103·3 : 1.
Differentials: One central 4 star.
Brakes
Foot: Power hydraulic, drum.
Hand: Mechanical on all wheels.
Steering
System: Recirculating ball hydraulic assisted.
Turning circle: R.H. 45′ (*13·72 metres*). L.H. 45′ (*13·72 metres*).
Suspension
Front: Independent all wheels by double wishbone and torsion bar.
Rear: Independent all wheels by double wishbone and torsion bar.
Shock absorbers: Telescopic hydraulic.
Towing Attachments
Type: Rear, hook.
Electrical Equipment
Generator: 2-speed 75 amp.
Batteries: 2 12 volt 60 A.H.
Suppression: To F.V.R.D.E. Specification 2051, Appendix D1, Schedule B.

MANUFACTURERS

Chassis: ⎫
Body: ⎭ ALVIS CO. LTD., Coventry.

ALTERNATIVE ROLES

1. Command vehicle.
2. Signals vehicle.
3. Armoured ambulance.
4. Radar vehicle.
5. Sonic deception vehicle.
6. Infantry command post.

Armoured Car 76 mm Gun
(Alvis Saladin Mk.2 6 x 6)
(Project State—In Service)

Description: This vehicle has been developed for use with infantry and armoured formations for reconnaissance and pursuit purposes, and is normally operated by a crew of three. The hull and turret are of welded armour plate construction. The vehicle can be waded to a depth of 3' 6" without preparation. The armament consists of a 76 m.m. quick firing gun and two ·30" machine guns. Stowage is provided in the hull for 43 rounds of ammunition. Periscopes are provided for closed-down operation. The vehicle possesses a high degree of cross-country mobility and has an adequate road performance.

F.V. Specification Number: Chassis 9203. Body 9203. Equipment 9203.

Height: 7' 10" (*2·39 m.*).   Length: vehicle only. 16' 1" (*4·9 m.*) gun front 17' 3½" (*5·27 m.*).
Width: 8' 5" (*2·515 m.*).   Wheelbase: 10' 0" (*3·05 m.*).

Track: all wheels 6′ 10″ (*2·03 m.*).
Weight: Unladen 23,072 lb. (*10,500 kg.*).   Laden: 25,536 lb. (*11,600 kg.*).

PERFORMANCE DATA

Speed, average maximum:
  Road 30 m.p.h. (*48 km./h.*).
  C.C. 20 m.p.h. (*32 km./h.*).
Range of action at average maximum speed: 250 miles (*400 km.*).
Gross power weight ratio (b.h.p. per ton): 14·04.
Maximum tractive effort, low gear (lb. per ton): 1,375.
Maximum climbing ability: 1 in 2·2.
Maximum gradient for stop and restart: 1 in 3·2.

TECHNICAL DATA

Power Unit
Type: Rolls-Royce, B80, Mk. 6A, gasoline.
Displacement: 5,670 c.c. (346 cu. in.).
Gross B.H.P.: 170 at 3,750 r.p.m.
Nett torque: 260 lb. ft. at 2,000 r.p.m.
Speed limited to: 3,750 r.p.m.
Ignition type: Coil, 24 volt.
Fuel System
Type: Mechanical lift pump.
Type of fuel: Gasoline.
Air cleaner: F.V. design oil bath.
Fuel capacity: 53 gallons (*241 litres*).
Engine Lubrication
System: Dry sump.
Engine Cooling
System: Pressurised.
Wheels
Rims: W.D. divided disc light alloy.
Tyres: 12·00″ × 20″ R.F.
Tyre pump: Compressor, engine driven.
Chains: Can be fitted.
Transmission
Clutch: Fluid coupling.
Gearbox: Pre-selector 5-speed.
Transfer box: Forward and reverse.
Transfer box ratios: 2·43 : 1.

Propeller shafts: Muff couplings.
Axles: Articulating shafts.
Ratios: Top 10·05 : 1, bottom 103·3 : 1.
Differentials: One central 4 star.
Brakes
Foot: Hydraulic, disc all wheels.
Hand: Mechanical all wheels.
Steering
System: Recirculating ball, hydraulic assisted.
Turning circle: R.H. 48′ (*14·63 metres*). L.H. 48′ (*14·63 metres*).
Suspension
Front: Independent all wheels by double wishbone and torsion bar.
Rear: Independent all wheels by double wishbone and torsion bar.
Shock absorbers: Hydraulic telescopic.
Towing Attachments
Type: Rear, hook.
Electrical Equipment
Generator: 2 speed 75 amp.
Batteries: 2 12 volt 60 A.H.
Suppression: To F.V.R.D.E. Specification 2051, Appendix D1, Schedule B.

MANUFACTURERS

Chassis: }
Body: } ALVIS CO. LTD., Coventry.

F.V. 601(C)

Armoured Car Floating (Alvis Saladin 6 x 6)
(Project State—Undergoing User Trials)

Description: This vehicle is identical to Exhibit No. 87 but is shown fitted with a floatation screen to enable the vehicle to cross water obstacles. The installation comprises a completely new wing line right round the vehicle on which a screen of the camera bellows type is mounted. The small hand winches provided enable the three man crew to raise and lower the screen unaided. Transparent slots are provided in the front to give clear visability when driving the vehicle on land. Water propulsion is by the road wheels only.

F.V. Specification Number: Chassis 9203. Body 9203. Equipment 9203.

Height: 7′ 10″ (*2·39 m.*).   Length: Vehicle only. 16′ 11″ (*5·16 m.*). 17′ 8½″ (*5·4 m.*) with Gun front.
Width: 8′ 8″ (*2·64 m.*).   Wheelbase: 10′ 0″ (*3·048 m.*).
Track: All wheels 6′ 10″ (*2·08 m.*).
Weight: Unladen 23,567 lb. (*10·710 kg.*).   Laden 26,040 lb. (*11,820 kg.*).

PERFORMANCE DATA

Speed, average maximum:
Road 30 m.p.h. (*48 km./h.*).
C.C. 20 m.p.h. (*32 km./h.*).
Range of action at average maximum speed: 250 miles (*400 km.*).
Gross power weight ratio (b.h.p. per ton): 13·75.
Maximum tractive effort, low gear (lb. per ton): 1,350.
Maximum climbing ability: 1 in 2·2.
Maximum gradient for stop and restart: 1 in 3·2.

TECHNICAL DATA

Power Unit
Type: Rolls-Royce, B80, Mk. 6A, gasoline.
Displacement: 5,670 c.c. (346 cu. in.).
Gross B.H.P.: 170 at 3,750 r.p.m.
Nett torque: 260 lb. ft. at 2,000 r.p.m.
Speed limited to: 3,750 r.p.m.
Ignition type: Coil, 24 volt.
Fuel System
Type: Mechanical lift pump.
Type of fuel: Gasoline.
Air cleaner: F.V. design oil bath.
Fuel capacity: 53 gallons (*241 litres*).
Engine Lubrication
System: Dry sump.
Engine Cooling
System: Pressurised.
Wheels
Rims: W.D. pattern divided disc.
Tyres: 12·00″ × 20″ R.F.
Tyre pump: Mechanical, engine driven.
Chains: May be fitted.
Transmission
Clutch: Fluid coupling.
Gearbox: Pre-selective 5-speed.
Transfer box: Forward and reverse.
Transfer box ratios: 2·43 : 1.

Transmission—*continued*
Propeller shafts: Muff coupling.
Axles: Articulating shafts.
Ratios: Top 10·05 : 1, bottom 103·2 : 1.
Differentials: One central 4 star.
Brakes
Foot: Hydraulic disc all wheels.
Hand: Mechanical all wheels.
Steering
System: Recirculating ball hydraulic assisted.
Turning circle: R.H. 48′ (*14·63 metres*). L.H. 48′ (*14·63 metres*).
Suspension
Front: Independent all wheels by double wishbone and torsion bar.
Rear: Independent all wheels by double wishbone and torsion bar.
Shock absorbers: Hydraulic telescopic.
Towing Attachments
Type: Rear, hook.
Electrical Equipment
Generator: 2-speed 75 amp.
Batteries: 2 12 volt 60 A.H.
Suppression: To F.V.R.D.E. Specification 2051, Appendix D1, Schedule B.

MANUFACTURERS

Chassis:
Body: } ALVIS CO. LTD., Coventry.
Screen: GARNER MOTORS, Sunbury.

Armoured Command Vehicle Heavy
(A.E.C. 10 ton 6 x 6)

(Project State—Under Development)

Description: This vehicle has been designed for staff and signals use and can contain a variety of specialist equipment installations. The hull, which is mounted on a left hand drive short wheelbase version of the A.E.C. Mk. 3 10 ton G.S. chassis, is thermally insulated and fitted with standard air conditioning units. External power supplies may be used via a protected panel at the rear. The exhibit is a prototype vehicle and does not embody all the latest design proposals.

Height: including roof rack 10′ 8″ (*3·25 m.*).   Length: 25′ 0″ (*7·6 m.*).
Width: 8′ 2½″ (*2·5 m.*).   Wheelbase: 12′ 6″ (*3·81 m.*).
Track: Front 6′ 6¾″ (*2·00 m.*).   Rear 6′ 9″ (*2·06 m.*).
Weight: Unladen 33,200 lb. (*15,100 kg.*).   Laden 41,000 lb. (*18·750 kg.*).

PERFORMANCE DATA

Speed, average maximum:
 Road 33 m.p.h. (*72 km./h.*).
 C.C. 12–15 m.p.h. (*19–24 km./h.*).
Range of action at average maximum speed: 300 miles (*470 km.*).
Gross power weight ratio (b.h.p. per ton): 12·3 (12·3 *cu./tonne*).
Maximum tractive effort, low gear (lb. per ton): 1,310.
Maximum climbing ability: 1 in 3.
Maximum gradient for stop and restart: 1 in 3.

TECHNICAL DATA

Power Unit
Type: A.E.C., AV.760., Diesel.
Displacement: 12,473 c.c. (761 cu. in.).
Gross B.H.P.: 226 at 2,200 r.p.m.
Nett torque: 555 lb. ft. at 1,500 r.p.m.
Governed speed: 2,200 r.p.m.
Ignition type: Compression.
Fuel System
Type: Lift pump.
Type of fuel: Diesel.
Air cleaner: Oil bath.
Fuel capacity: 50 gallons (*227·5 litres*).
Engine Lubrication
System: Wet sump.
Engine Cooling
System: Pressurised.
Wheels
Rims: W.D. divided disc.
Tyres: 14·00″ × 20″ run flat.
Tyre pump: Air brake compressor.
Chains: Non-skid front, overall rear.
Transmission
Clutch: Single dry plate, air assisted operation.
Gearbox: 6 forward and 1 reverse speed.
Transfer box: 2-speed.
Transfer box ratios: 1 : 1, 1·62 : 1.
Propeller shafts: Hardy Spicer.

Transmission—*continued*
Axles: Fully floating.
Ratios: top 7·9 : 1, bottom 91·5 : 1.
Differentials: Three.
Differential locks: Inter axle on rear bogie.
Brakes
Foot: 2 line air pressure.
Hand: Mechanical on rear wheels, air assisted operation.
Trailer: 2 line air pressure.
Warning device: Buzzer and gauge.
Steering
System: Worm and nut, hydraulic assisted operation.
Turning circle: R.H. 66′ (*20·12 metres*). L.H. 66′ (*20·12 metres*).
Suspension
Front: Semi-elliptic
Rear: Inverted semi-elliptic
Shock absorbers: Hydraulic, front only.
Towing Attachments
Type: Front, hook. Rear, hook.
Electrical Equipment
Generator: Generator No. 10 Mk. 2 (AC 7/90).
Batteries: No. 4, Mk. 3 (U K 6 TN).
Suppression: F.V.R.D.E.
Specification 2501, Appendix D1, Schedule A.

MANUFACTURERS

Chassis: A.E.C. LTD., Southall, Middx.
Body: ROF, Barnbow, Leeds.

Truck Cargo HMLC (Alvis Stalwart Mk. 2 6 x 6)

(Project State—1st off Production June 1966)

Description: This vehicle is a further development of the Mk. 1 incorporating modifications suggested during the course of trials and operational experience. It is similar to the Mk. 1 but has better visibility, improved cab layout, further improved reliability, reduced maintenance load and a self recovery winch. Water speed has been increased to 6¼ m.p.h. by using more efficient propulsion units. The cab seats two with provision for a third seat if required.

F.V. Specification Number: Chassis 9331. Body 9331. Equipment 9331.

Height: 8′ 4″ (*2·54 m.*).   Length: 20′ 10″ (*6·35 m.*).
Width: 8′ 7″ (*2·62 m.*).   Wheelbase: 10′ 0″ (*3·05 m.*).
Track: 6′ 8″ (*2·03 m.*).
Weight: Unladen 19,600 lb. (*8,890 kg.*). Laden: 31,890 *lb.* (*14·350 kh.*).

PERFORMANCE DATA

Speed, average maximum:
　　Road 30 m.p.h. (*48 km./h.*).　C.C. 20 m.p.h. (*32 km./h.*).
Range of action at average maximum speed: 250 miles (*400 km.*).
Gross power weight ratio (b.h.p. per ton): 16.
Maximum tractive effort, low gear (lb. per ton): 1,210 (100% efficiency nett torque).
Maximum climbing ability: 1 in 2·2.
Maximum gradient for stop and restart: 1 in 3·2.

TECHNICAL DATA

Power Unit
Type: Rolls-Royce, B81, Mk. 8B, gasoline.
Displacement: 6,522 c.c. (398 cu. in.).
Gross B.H.P.: 220 at 3,750 r.p.m.
Nett torque: 315 lb. ft. at 2,250 r.p.m.
Speed limited to: 3,750 r.p.m.
Ignition type: Coil, 24 volt.
Fuel System
Type: Mechanical Pump.
Type of fuel: Gasoline.
Air cleaner: FV design twin oil bath.
Fuel capacity: 100 gallons (455 *litres*).
Engine Lubrication
System: Dry sump,.
Engine Cooling
System: Pressurised.
Wheels
Rims: WD light alloy divided disc 10·00″ × 20″.
Tyres: 14·00″ × 20″ 14 ply pneumatic.
Tyre pump: Engine compressor.
Transmission
Clutch: Twin plate, friction.
Gearbox: 5-speed synchromesh on 2, 3, 4 and 5.
Transfer box: Bevel and helical with forward and reverse.
Transfer box ratios: 3·13 : 1.
Propeller shafts: 4 internal with muff couplings.

Axles: 6 drive shafts with inner and outer Tracta Joints.
Ratios: top 12·9 : 1, bottom 103·3 : 1.
Differentials: Across vehicle none fore and aft.
Differential locks: 'No spin' type.
Brakes
Foot: Air over hydraulic 15″ disc on all wheels.
Hand: Contracting band on drums on front bevel boxes.
Steering
System: Recirculating ball, hydraulically assisted, front 4 wheels.
Turning circle: R.H. 55′ (*17·15 metres*). L.H. 55′ (*17·15 metres*).
Suspension
Front: Independent all wheels by double wishbone and torsion bar.
Rear: Independent all wheels by double wishbone and torsion bar.
Shock absorbers: Hydraulic telescopic, bump and rebound telescopic stops.
Towing Attachments
Type: Rear,hook.
Electrical Equipment
Generator: 24 volt alternator 50 amp.
Batteries: 2 × 12 volt 6TN 100 A.H.
Suppression: T9 F.V.R.D.E.
Specification 2051, Appendix D1, Schedule B.

MANUFACTURERS

Chassis: ⎫
Body: ⎭　ALVIS CO. LTD., Coventry.

ALTERNATIVE ROLES

1. Artillery limber with crane.

Tractor Wheeled General Service, for 8in. Howitzer (Leyland 10 ton 6 x 6)
(Project State—Production Authorized)

Description: The vehicle has the same basic chassis and winch as Exhibit Nos. 92 and 98. Its main role is to tow the Heavy Artillery 8″ Howitzer. A crew of 11 can be accommodated (3 in cab, 8 in body). The steel body has been designed to give a low silhouette and to carry ammunition, equipment and stores. Two side doors facilitate speedy entry and exit of the crew. A special rear towing attachment is fitted to match the 8″ Howitzer, when towed without a limber. A chain hoist is provided to enable the gun trail to be raised into its towing position. When towed with a limber an alternative towing hook can be fitted.

F.V. Specification Number: Chassis 9332. Body 9332.

Height: U.L. 10′ 5½″ (*3·19 m.*).　Length: 27′ 0″ (*8·23 m.*).
Width: 8′ 6″ (*2·59 m.*).　Wheelbase: 14′ 6″ (*4·42 m.*).
Track: Front 6′ 10¼″ (*2·09 m.*).　Rear 6′ 10¼″ (*2·09 m.*).
Weight: Unladen estimated 31,528 lb. (*14,310 kg.*).

PERFORMANCE DATA

Speed, average maximum:
  Road 26 m.p.h. (*41·8 km./h.*). C.C. 15 m.p.h. (*24·1 km./h.*).
Range of action at average maximum speed: 350 miles (*563 km.*).
Gross power weight-ratio (b.h.p. per ton):
Maximum tractive effort, low gear (lb. per ton): 1,060 (100% efficiency).
Maximum climbing ability: 1 in 4 ⎫
Maximum gradient for stop and restart: 1 in 4 ⎬ with 8″ Howitzer.

TECHNICAL DATA

Power Unit
Type: Rolls-Royce, B81, Mk. 5H, gasoline.
Displacement: 6,522 c.c. (398 cu. in.).
Gross B.H.P.: 195 at 3,750 r.p.m.
Nett torque: 308 lb. ft. at 2,150 r.p.m.
Speed limited to: 3,750 r.p.m.
Ignition type: Coil 24 volt.
Fuel System
Type: Lift pump.
Type of Fuel: Gasoline.
Air Cleaner: Oil bath.
Fuel capacity: 98 gallons. (*445 litres*).
Engine Lubrication
System: Wet sump.
Engine Cooling
System: Pressurised.
Wheels
Rims: 4-piece disc.
Tyres: 15·00″ × 20″ c.c.
Tyre pump: Air brake compressor.
Chains: Non-skid front, overall rear.
Transmission
Clutch: Twin plate, 12″ dia. (*305 mm.*).
Gearbox: 4-speed synchromesh, 1 reverse.

Transfer box: 3-speed.
Transfer box ratios: 1·055 : 1, 1·36 : 1, 2·9 : 1.
Propeller shafts: Hardy Spicer.
Axles: Driven front and rear.
Ratios: top 14·9 : 1, bottom 190·4 : 1.
Differentials: Two.
Brakes
Foot: 2 line air pressure.
Hand: Mechanical, disc type on transmission.
Trailer: Air pressure.
Warning Device: Light.
Steering
System: Cam and roller, hydraulic power assistance.
Turning Circle: R.H. 70′ (*21·3 metres*). L.H. 70′ (*21·3 metres*).
Suspension
Front: Transverse semi-elliptic spring
Rear: Semi-elliptic springs.
Towing Attachments
Type: Front, hook. Rear, hook.
Electrical Equipment
Generator: 24 volt.
Batteries: 24 volt.
Suppression: To F.V.R.D.E. Specification 2051, Appendix D1, Schedule B.

MANUFACTURERS

Chassis: LEYLAND MOTORS LTD., Leyland.
Body: MARSHALLS CAMBRIDGE (ENGINEERING) LTD.

Truck Cargo Dropside (Leyland 10 ton 6 x 6)
(Project State—Vehicles in Service)

Description: The chassis and winch of this vehicle are identical to that of the F.V. 1103 Tractor Medium Artillery Exhibit No. 98. The body is 16′ 0″ (*4·88 m.*) long and 8′ 0″ (*2·44 m.*) wide internally and has been designed to facilitate side and end loading with mechanical handling aids, drop sides and removable pillars being provided for this purpose. Because of its good mobility, powerful winch and front and rear towing hooks this vehicle would be suitable for bridging operations.

F.V. Specification Number: Chassis 9278. Body 9278.

Height: 11′ 9″ (*3·58 m.*).   Length: 27′ 6″ (*8·38 m.*).
Width: 8′ 6″ (*2·59 m.*).   Wheelbase: 14′ 6″ (*4·42 m.*).
Track: Front 6′ 10¼″ (*2·09 m.*).   Rear 6′ 10¼″ (*2·09 m.*).
Weight: Unladen 31,528 lb. (*14,310 kg.*). Laden 53,928 lb. (*24,600 kg.*).

PERFORMANCE DATA
Speed, average maximum:
    Road 26 m.p.h. (*41·8 km./h.*).   C.C. 15 m.p.h. (*24·1 km./h.*).

Range of action at average maximum speed: 350 miles (*563 km.*).
Gross power weight ratio (b.h.p. per ton): 9·56.
Maximum tractive effort, low gear (lb. per ton): 1,060.
Maximum climbing ability: 1 in 2.
Maximum gradient for stop and restart: 1 in 3.

TECHNICAL DATA

Power Unit
Type: Rolls-Royce B81, Mk. 5H, gasoline.
Displacement: 6,522 c.c. (398 cu. in.).
Gross B.H.P.: 195 at 3,750 r.p.m.
Nett torque: 308 lb. ft. at 2,150 r.p.m.
Speed limited to: 3,750 r.p.m.
Ignition type: Coil 24 volt.

Fuel System
Type: Lift pump.
Type of fuel: Gasoline.
Air cleaner: Oil bath.
Fuel capacity 98 gallons (*445 litres*).

Engine Lubrication
System: Wet sump.

Engine Cooling
System: Pressurised.

Wheels
Rims: 4 piece disc pattern.
Tyres: 15·00″ × 20″ C.C.
Type pump: Air brake compressor.
Chains: Non-skid front, overall rear.

Transmission
Clutch: Twin plate, 12″ dia. (*305 mm.*).
Gearbox: 4-speed synchromesh, 1 reverse.

Transfer box: 3-speed.
Transfer box ratios: 1·055 : 1, 1·36 : 1, 2·9 : 1.
Propeller shafts: Hardy Spicer.
Axles: Driven front and rear.
Ratios: top 14·9 : 1, bottom 190·4 : 1.
Differentials: Two.

Brakes
Foot: 2 line air pressure.
Hand: Mechanical, disc type on transmission.
Trailer: Air pressure.
Warning device: light.

Steering
System: Cam and roller, hydraulic power assistance.
Turning circle: R.H. 70′ (*21·3 metres*). L.H. 70′ (*21·3 metres*).

Suspension
Front: Transverse semi-elliptic spring.
Rear: Semi-elliptic springs.

Towing Attachments
Type: Front, hook. Rear, hook.

Electrical Equipment
Generator: 24 volt.
Batteries: 24 volt.
Suppression: To F.V.R.D.E. Specification 2051, Appendix D1, Schedule B.

MANUFACTURERS

Chassis: LEYLAND MOTORS LTD., Leyland.
Body: MARSHALLS CAMBRIDGE (ENGINEERING) LTD.

Truck Cargo with Winch
(AEC 10 ton Mk. 3, 6 x 6)
(Project State—Under Development)

Description: The chassis and cab for this vehicle is shown at Exhibit No. 94. The body has a flat floor having an internal length of 20′ 6″ (*6·25 m.*) and width of 7′ 8″ (*2·34 m.*) and is intended for the carriage of all forms of cargo. To facilitate loading by fork lift truck the body sides in addition to the tailboard may be dropped down or removed. The vehicle shown is fitted with a 7 ton direct pull power driven winch with 250′ (*76·3 m.*) of rope and towing hooks front and rear. In this condition the vehicle is particularly suitable for use in bridge building and bridge transport operations.

Height: 11′ 6″ (*3·50 m.*).   Length: 29′ 9″ (*9·08 m.*).
Width: 8′ 2″ (*2·49 m.*).   Wheelbase: 16′ 0″ (*4·88 m.*).
Track: Front 6′ 6¾″ (*2·0 m.*).   Rear 6′ 9″ (*2·06 m.*).
Weight: (Estimated) Unladen 26.104 lb. (*11,850 kg.*).
(Estimated) Laden 48,504 lb. (*22,000 kg.*).

PERFORMANCE DATA

Speed, average maximum:
 Road 33 m.p.h. (*53·1 km./h.*). C.C. 15 m.p.h. (*24·1 km./h.*).
Range of action at average maximum speed: 300 miles (*483 km.*).
Gross power weight ratio (b.h.p. per ton): 10.
Maximum tractive effort, low gear (lb. per ton: 1,200.
Maximum climbing ability: 1 in 3.
Maximum gradient for stop and restart: 1 in 3.

TECHNICAL DATA

Power Unit
Type: A.E.C., AV760, Diesel.
Displacement: 12,473 c.c. (761 cu.in.).
Gross B.H.P.: 226 at 2,200 r.p.m.
Nett torque: 555 lb. ft. at 1,500 r.p.m.
Governed speed: 2,200 r.p.m.
Ignition type: Compression.
Fuel System
Type: Lift pump.
Type of fuel: Diesel.
Air cleaner: Oil bath.
Fuel capacity: 48 gallons (*218 litres*).
Engine Lubrication
System: Wet sump.
Engine Cooling
System: Pressurised.
Wheels
Rims: WD divided disc.
Tyres: 15·00″ × 20″ c.c. (alternative 14·00″ or 16·00″ × 20″).
Tyre Pump: Air brake compressor.
Chains: non-skid front, overall rear.
Transmission
Clutch: Single dry plate.
Gearbox: 6-speed constant mesh. 1 reverse.
Transfer box: 2-speed.
Transfer box ratios: 1·1 : 1 and 1·62 : 1.

Propeller shafts: Hardy Spicer.
Axles: Fully floating.
Ratios: top 7·9 : 1, bottom 91·5 : 1.
Differentials: Three.
Brakes
Foot: 2 line air pressure, dual circuit.
Hand: Mechanical on four rear wheels, air pressure assisted.
Trailer: Air pressure.
Warning device: Buzzer and Gauge.
Steering
System: Worm and nut hydraulic assistance.
Turning circle: R.H. 75′ (*22·8 metres*). L.H. 75′ (*22·8 metres*).
Suspension
Front: Semi-elliptic springs.
Rear: Semi-elliptic springs inverted.
Shock absorbers: Front only.
Towing Attachments
Type: Front, hook. Rear, hook.
Electrical Equipment
Generator: 5″ dia. 25 amp. Alternative 7″ dia. 90 amp.
Batteries: 24 volt.
Suppression: To F.V.R.D.E.
Specification 2051, Appendix D1. Schedule B.

MANUFACTURERS

Chassis: A.E.C. LTD., Southall, Middlesex.
Body: MARSHALLS OF CAMBRIDGE (ENGINEERING) LTD.
Cab: PARK ROYAL VEHICLES LTD.

ALTERNATIVE ROLES

Bulk fuel carrier
Refueller
Tractor
Recovery Vehicle } In short wheel base form
Command Vehicle

195

Chassis Wheeled Self Propelled
(AEC 10 ton Mk. 3 6 x 6)

(Project State—Under Development)

Description: This vehicle chassis/cab is the successor to the 10 ton 6 × 6 A.E.C. Mk. 1 and has been built to comply with the essential requirements of the F.V.R.D.E. basic 10 ton G.S. vehicle specification. The design embodies current commercial vehicle components adapted as necessary to meet military requirements. The vehicle dimensions permit the fitting of a flat floor cargo body having an internal length of 20′ 6″ (*6·25 m.*) and width of 7′ 8″ (*2·34 m.*) as shown by Exhibit No. 93.

Chassis/Cab only—height (over cab): 9′ 5″ (*2·87 m.*).   Length: 29′ 3″ (*8·91 m.*).

Width: 8′ 0″ (*2·44 m.*).   Wheelbase: 16′ 0″ (*4·88 m.*).

Track: Front 6′ 6¾″ (*2·0 m.*).   Rear 6′ 9″ (*2·06 m.*).

Weight: 19,088 lb. (*8,670 kg.*).

PERFORMANCE DATA

Speed, average maximum:
    Road   C.C.
Range of action at average maximum speed
Gross power weight ratio (b.h.p. per ton)
Maximum tractive effort, low gear (lb. per ton)
Maximum climbing ability
Maximum gradient for stop and restart

} Refer to Exhibit No. 93

TECHNICAL DATA

Power Unit
Type: A.E.C., AV760, Diesel.
Displacement: 12,473 c.c. (761 cu. in.).
Gross B.H.P.: 226 at 2,200 r.p.m.
Nett torque: 555 lb. ft. at 1,500 r.p.m.
Governed speed: 2,200 r.p.m.
Ignition type: Compression.
Fuel System
Type: Lift pump.
Type of fuel: Diesel.
Air cleaner: Oil bath.
Fuel capacity: 48 gallons (*218 litres*).
Engine Lubrication.
System: Wet sump.
Engine Cooling
System: Pressurised.
Wheels
Rims: WD divided disc.
Tyres: 15·00″ × 20″ C.C. (alternative 14·00″ × 20″, 16·00″ × 20″).
Tyre pump: Air brake compressor.
Chains: Non-skid front, overall rear.
Transmission.
Clutch: Single dry plate.
Gearbox: 6-speed constant mesh, 1 reverse.
Transfer box: 2-speed.
Transfer box ratios: 1·1 : 1 and 1·62 : 1.

Transmission—*continued*
Propeller shafts: Hardy Spicer.
Axles: Fully floating.
Ratios: top: 7·9, bottom: 91·5.
Differentials: Three.
Brakes.
Foot: 2 line air pressure dual circuit.
Hand: Mechanical on 4 rear wheels, air pressure assisted.
Trailer: Air pressure.
Warning device: Buzzer and Gauge.
Steering
System: Worm and nut, hydraulic assistance.
Turning Circle: R.H. 75′ (*22·8 metres*). L.H. 75′ (*22·8 metres*).
Suspension
Front: Semi elliptic springs.
Rear: Semi-elliptic springs inverted.
Shock Absorbers: Front only.
Towing Attachments
Type: Front, hook. Rear, hook.
Electrical Equipment
Generator: 5″ dia. 25 amp. Alternative 7″ dia. 90 amp.
Batteries: 24 volt.
Suppression: To F.V.R.D.E. Specification 2051, Appendix DI, Schedule B.

MANUFACTURERS

Chassis: A.E.C. LTD., Southall, Middlesex.
Cab: PARK ROYAL VEHICLES LTD.

ROLES

Bulk Fuel Carrier.
Refueller.
Cargo Carrier.
Tractor
Recovery Vehicle
Command Vehicle

} In short wheel base form.

Chassis Wheeled, Self Propelled
(Leyland 10 ton 6 x 6, S.W.B.)
(Project State—Under Assessment)

Description: The chassis shown is a short wheelbase 10-ton 6×6 commercial vehicle which has been developed by the manufacturer to meet military requirements. It is suitable for use as a Tractor (Medium Artillery); Tractor for full or semi trailer; Medium Recovery Tractor or Tipper. A long wheelbase (15′ 6″, *4·72 m.*) version for cargo and tanker roles is also available. Both versions may be fitted with a power driven winch.

Height: 9′ 9″ (*2·97 m.*).
Length: 24′ 9″ (chassis/cab) (*7·54 m.*).
Width: 8′ 0″ (*2·44 m.*).
Wheelbase: 13′ 3″ (*4·04 m.*).
Track: Front 6′ 4″ (*1·93 m.*).   Rear 6′ 1″ (*1·85 m.*).
Weight: Unladen 18,816 lb. (*8,467 kg.*).   Laden: 47,600 lb. (*21,420 kg.*).

PERFORMANCE DATA

Speed, average maximum:
    Road 33 m.p.h. (*53 km/h.*).
    C.C. 12 m.p.h. (*19·31 km/h.*).
Range of action at average maximum speed: 300 miles (*480 km.*).
Gross power weight ratio (b.h.p. per ton): *10*.
Maximum tractive effort, low gear (lb. per ton): 1,130.
Maximum climbing ability: 1 in 1·9.
Maximum gradient for stop and restart: 1 in 2.

TECHNICAL DATA

Power Unit
Type: Leyland, 0·680, Diesel.
Displacement: 11,100 c.c. (677 cu. in.).
Gross B.H.P.: 216 at 2,200 r.p.m.
Nett torque: 548 lb. ft. at 1,400 r.p.m.
Governed speed: 2,200 r.p.m.
Ignition type: Compression.

Fuel System
Type: Mechanical lift pump.
Type of fuel: Diesel.
Air Cleaner: Oil bath.
Fuel capacity: 48 gallons (*218 litres*).

Engine Lubrication
System: Wet sump.

Engine Cooling
System: Pressurised.

Wheels
Rims: 10·00 × 20. 4 piece disc.
Tyres: 14·00 × 20 C.C. 18 ply.
Tyre pump: Air brake reservoir.
Chains: Non-skid.

Transmission
Clutch: Single dry plate.
Gearbox: Seven forward one reverse.

Transmission—*continued*
Transfer box: On main gearbox.
Propeller shafts: Hardy Spicer.
Axles: Fully floating.
Ratios: top 8·77 : 1, bottom 81·46 : 1.
Differentials: Four.

Brakes
Foot: 2 line air pressure.
Hand: Mechanical—power assisted.
Trailer: 2 line air pressure.
Warning device: Audible.

Steering
System: Cam and double roller.
Turning circle: R.H. 66′ (*19·8 metres*). L.H. 64′ (*19·2 metres*).

Suspension
Front: Semi-elliptic.
Rear: Inverted semi-elliptic.

Towing Attachments
Type: Rear, hook.

Electrical Equipment
Generator: C.A.V. Model GL.45/24/1 4½″ waterproofed 24 volt.
Batteries: 4×6 volt lead/acid, 121 amp hours (10 hr. rating).

MANUFACTURERS

Chassis: LEYLAND MOTORS LTD., Leyland, Lancs.

Truck, Missile Transporter (AEC 10 ton 4 x 2)

(Project State—In Service)

Description: The vehicle is based on an A.E.C. Mandator chassis with type AV.690 diesel engine, heavy duty rear axle and power-assisted steering. It is fitted with a rubber-mounted superstructure for transporting, loading and unloading the Blue Steel missile. During handling of the missile the superstructure is supported on the ground by four hydraulically operated jack legs and the suspension retracted by hydraulic jacks to bring the wheels clear of the ground. The davit is mechanially operated from the vehicle engine via the power take-off and a special clutch, brake and gearbox unit. The missile is held between a pair of hydraulically retractable trestles and a resilient mounting in the davit head to ensure a correct clamping load. A series of interlocks ensure that the loading and unloading operations are carried out in the correct sequence.

F.V. Specification Number: Chassis 9271. Body 9271. Equipment 9271.

Height: 12′ 6″ (*3·81 m.*).   Length: 30′ 6″ (*9·30 m.*) Unladen.
Width: 9′ 0″ (*2·74 m.*) Unladen.   Wheelbase: 19′ 0″ (*5·80 m.*).
Track: Front 6′ 6½″ (*2·0 m.*).   Rear: 6′ 6″ (*1·98 m.*).
Weight: Unladen 36,500 lb. (*16,500 kg.*).

PERFORMANCE DATA

Speed, maximum, road: 17½ m.p.h. (laden).
Range of action at average maximum speed: 300 miles (*480 km.*).
Gross power weight ratio (b.h.p. per ton) (unladen): 11·0.
Maximum tractive effort, low gear (lb. per ton) (unladen): 903.
Maximum gradient for stop and restart (unladen): 1 in 3.

TECHNICAL DATA

Power Unit
Type: A.E.C., AV.690, Diesel.
Displacement: 11,310 c.c. (690 cu. in.)
Gross B.H.P.: 179 at 1,800 r.p.m.
Nett torque: 480 lb. ft. at 1,200 r.p.m.
Governed Speed: 1,800 r.p.m.
Ignition type: Compression.

Fuel System
Type: Pressure feed.
Type of Fuel: Diesel.
Air Cleaner: Oil bath.
Fuel capacity: 45 gallons (*205 litres*).

Engine Lubrication
System: Wet sump.

Engine Cooling
System: Pressurised.

Wheels
Rims: 10·00″ × 20″, 3 piece.
Tyres: G.20 14·00″ × 20″, conducting type.
Tyre Pump: Air brake compressor.

Transmission
Clutch: Single dry plate.
Gearbox: 5 forward, 1 reverse.
Propeller shafts: Hardy Spicer.

Transmission—*continued*
Axles: Driven rear, double reduction.
Ratios: Top 7·92 : 1, bottom 52·2 : 1.
Differentials: One.

Brakes
Foot: Air pressure, dual system.
Hand: Mechanical and air on rear axle only.
Warning device: Visual.

Steering
System: Worm and nut, power assisted.
Turning circle: R.H. 84′ (*25·6 metres*). L.H. 72′ (*22 metres*).

Suspension
Front: Semi-elliptic.
Rear: Semi-elliptic with Aeon rubber assistors.

Towing Attachments
Type: Rear, special multi-level.

Electrical Equipment
Nominal 24 volt D.C. two wire insulated return.
Generator: CAV G7B24/23X.
Batteries: 4 × 6 volt.
Suppression: To F.V.R.D.E.
Specification 2051, Appendix D1, Schedule B.

MANUFACTURERS

A.E.C. LTD., Southall, Middx.

Chassis AEC 10 ton 6 x 6 with special tipping platform body R.E. (Bri-Mec)

(Project State—Under Development)

Description: The vehicle illustrated has a prototype tilting body for use by the Royal Engineers. It is mounted on a 10 ton 6 × 6 A.E.C. Mk. 1 chassis which has been used because of its availability for the initial production. For future production the Bri-Mec body would be mounted on the A.E.C. Mk. 3 chassis Exhibit No. 94. A general purpose cargo body with removable drop sides is mounted on an underframe and the whole unit can be moved hydraulically rearwards and be tilted until the rear end touches the ground. In this position vehicles, tracked or wheeled, can be driven or winched on and the body returned to its forward position. When not being used for this purpose the vehicle can be utilised for general transportation duties.

Height: Over cab 9′ 4½″ (*2·86 m.*).   Length: 30′ 0″ (*9·14 m.*).
Width: 8′ 2″ (*2·49 m.*).   Wheelbase: 16′ 0″ (*4·88 m.*).
Track: Front 6′ 6½″ (*1·99 m.*).   Rear 6′ 3¼″ (*1·91 m.*).
Weight: Laden 45,500 lb. (Max) (*20,660 kg.*).

PERFORMANCE DATA

Speed, average maximum:
    Road 24 m.p.h. (*38·62 km./h.*).
    C.C. 12 m.p.h. (*19·31 km./h.*).
Range of Action at average maximum speed: 300 miles (*483 km.*).
Maximum tractive effort, low gear (lb. per ton); 1,100.
Maximum climbing ability: 1 in 3.
Maximum gradient for stop and restart: 1 in 3.
Gross power weight ratio (b.h.p. per ton) 7·5.

TECHNICAL DATA

Power Unit
Type: A.E.C., 11·3 *litre* A223, Diesel.
Displacement: 11,310 c.c. (690 cu. in.).
Gross B.H.P.: 152 at 1800 r.p.m.
Nett torque: 480 lb. ft. at 1,100 r.p.m.
Governed speed: 1,800 r.p.m.
Ignition Type: Compression.

Fuel System
Type: Lift pump.
Type of fuel: Diesel.
Air cleaner: Oil bath.
Fuel capacity: 48 gallons (218 *litres*).

Engine Lubrication
System: Wet sump.

Engine Cooling
System: Pressurised.

Wheels
Rims: Divided disc.
Tyres: 14·00″ × 20″ c.c. or 15·00″ × 20 c.c.
Tyre pump: Air brake compressor.
Chains: Non-skid front, overall rear.

Transmission
Clutch: Single plate—dry.
Gearbox: 5 forward, 1 reverse.
Transfer box: 2-speed.

Transmission—*continued*
Transfer box ratios: 1 : 1 and 1·62 : 1.
Propeller shafts: Hardy Spicer.
Axles: 3 driven.
Ratios: top 7·9 : 1, bottom 84·5 : 1.
Differentials: Three.

Brakes
Foot: 2 line air pressure.
Hand: Mechanical on rear wheels.
Trailer: Air pressure.
Warning device: Light.

Steering
System: Worm and nut.
Turning circle: R.H. 75′ (22·8 *metres*). L.H. 75′ (22·8 *metres*).

Suspension
Front: Semi-elliptic springs.
Rear: Semi-elliptic springs, inverted.
Shock Absorbers: Front only.

Towing Attachments
Type: Front, hook.

Electrical Equipment
Generator: 5″ dia. D.C.
Batteries: 24 volt.
Suppression: To F.V.R.D.E.
Specification 2051, Appendix D1, Schedule B.

MANUFACTURERS

Chassis: A.E.C. LTD., Southall, Middx.
Body: MICKLEOVER TRANSPORT LTD., Park Royal.
Specialist Equipment: BRISTOL METAL CONTRACTS LTD., Bristol, 5.

Tractor Wheeled General Service Medium Artillery (Leyland 10 ton 6 x 6)

(Project State—Vehicles in Service)

Description: This vehicle was developed to meet a requirement for towing medium artillery over heavy and severe cross-country terrain. The chassis is fitted with a 10 ton winch, driven from a power take off and having 350′ (*107 m.*) of rope. The body has seating for a total crew of twelve; stowage for personal kit and small-arms being provided. In addition 4½ tons (*4,580 kg.*) of ammunition and stores may be carried.

F.V. Specification Number: Chassis 9078. Body 9579.

Height: 10′ 1″ (*3·07 m.*).   Length: 26′ 10¼″ (*8·18 m.*).
Width: 8′ 6″ (*2·59 m.*).   Wheelbase: 14′ 6″ (*4·42 m.*).
Track: Front 6′ 10¼″ (*2·09 m.*).   Rear 6′ 10¼″ (*2·09 m.*).
Weight: Unladen 31,528 lb. (*14,310 kg.*). Laden 41,100 lb. (*18·660 kg.*).

PERFORMANCE DATA

Speed, average maximum:
Road 26 m.p.h. (*41·8 km./h.*). C.C. 15 m.p.h. (*24·1 km./h.*).
Range of action at average Maximum speed: 350 miles (*564 km.*).
Gross Power weight ratio (b.h.p. per ton): 11·7
Maximum tractive effort, low gear (lb. per ton): 1,650.
Maximum climbing ability: 1 in 2.
Maximum gradient for stop and restart: 1 in 3.

TECHNICAL DATA

Power Unit
Type: Rolls-Royce B81, Mk. 5H, gasoline.
Displacement: 6,522 c.c. (398 cu. in.).
Gross B.H.P.: 195 at 3,750 r.p.m.
Nett torque: 308 lb. ft. at 2,150 r.p.m.
Speed limited to : 3,750 r.p.m.
Ignition type: Coil, 24 volt.
Fuel System
Type: Lift pump
Type of fuel: Gasoline.
Air cleaner: Oil bath
Fuel capacity: 98 gallons (*445 litres*).
Engine Lubrication
System: Wet sump.
Engine Cooling
System: Pressurised.
Wheels
Rims: 4 piece disc pattern.
Tyres: 15·00″ × 20″ C.C.
Tyre pump: Air brake compressor.
Chains: Non-skid front, overall rear.
Transmission
Clutch: Twin plate 12″ dia. (*305 mm.*).
Gearbox: 4 speed synchromesh, 1 reverse.

Transfer box: 3 speed.
Transfer box ratios: 1·055 : 1, 1·36 : 1, 2·9 : 1.
Propeller shafts: Hardy Spicer.
Axles: Driven front and rear.
Ratios: Top 14·9 : 1, Bottom 190·4 : 1.
Differentials: Two.
Brakes
Foot: 2 line air pressure.
Hand: Mechanical, disc type on transmission.
Trailer: Air pressure.
Warning device: Light.
Steering
System: Cam and roller, hydraulic power assistance.
Turning circle: R.H. 70′ (*21·3 metres*), L.H. 70′ (*21·3 metres*).
Suspension
Front: Transverse semi-elliptic spring.
Rear: Semi-elliptic springs.
Towing Attachments
Type: Front: hook, Rear: hook.
Electrical Equipment
Generator: 24 volt.
Batteries: 24 volt.
Suppression: To F.V.R.D.E. Specification 2051, Appendix D1, Schedule B.

MANUFACTURERS

Chassis: LEYLAND MOTORS LTD., Leyland.
Body: PARK ROYAL VEHICLES LTD.

ALTERNATIVE ROLES

Basic chassis for recovery vehicles.
Basic chassis (long wheel base) for cargo carrier.

Chieftain

Description: A heavily armoured main battle tank, carrying a crew of 4 and mounting a 120 mm. high velocity gun firing APDS and HESH/ HE bagged charge ammunition. 53 rounds can be stowed, the bagged charges being carried in fire-suppressing containers. The fire control system incorporates a ranging machine gun which is integral with the main armament and is linked to the sight which has graticule marking appropriate to a simple ranging machine gun technique that enables a high chance of hit to be achieved with the main armament.

A contra-rotating cupola provides good all-round vision for the Commander and enables him to give rapid target indication to the gunner. Alternatively, he can aim and fire the gun himself by means of a sight which is optically linked to the gunner's sight. The gun control systems stabilises the turret in azimuth and the gun in elevation and enables accurate firing 'on the move' to be achieved. The vehicle is powered by a L.60 multi-fuel engine.

Height: 9′ 6″ (*2·89 m.*).   Length: (hull) 24′ 8″ (*7·52 m.*).
Width: 11′ 6″ (*3·50 m.*).
Weight: Laden 115,600 lb.   Unladen 110,760 lb.

52·44 Tonnes   206

105 m.m. Field Artillery Self-Propelled

Description: The Abbot, a self-propelled 105 mm. gun, is one of a family of light-armoured tracked vehicles. The automotive equipment includes a two-stroke multi-fuel engine which can use diesel fuel or petrol. The vehicle has a built-in flotation screen permitting deep water, river or estuary crossings. The crew of four are provided with ventilation and cooling facilities for extreme climatic operation. Eight prototypes are undergoing extensive User Trials.

Height: 8′ 9″ (*2·65 m.*)   Length: 19′ 2″ (*5·83 m.*).
Width: 8′ 8″ (*2·64 m.*).   Track: Centres 7′ 2″ (*2·18 m.*).
Weight: Unladen 34,000 lb. Laden 38,500 lb.

Ambulance Role

Description: In this role provision is made for carrying four stretchers, two either side. Alternatively two stretchers one side with five seating compartments on the other side. Approximate laden weight as for the APC.

F.V. 432
Armoured Personnel Carrier and Carl-Gustav Role

Description: The F.V. 432 APC is a lightweight fully tracked vehicle providing armoured protection to infantry detachments. The hull is constructed of steel armoured plate of sufficient thickness to give protection against shell fragments, flash burns and small arms fire. It is powered by a K60 No. 4 Mk. 4F Rolls-Royce multi-fuel engine. It has forced ventilation with individual diffusers to each of the personnel. This ventilation system will be capable of having a single or double heater or alternatively a refrigeration unit 'buttoned' into the line. The Commander's cupola mounts a G.P.M.G. or modified Bren and has a 360° traverse. The APC is the basic vehicle of a family and can be converted into the following roles:—

Wombat	Exhibit No. 109	Ambulance	Exhibit No. 101
Mortar	Exhibit No. 103	Carl-Gustav	Exhibit No. 102
Command Post	Exhibit No. 104	Recovery	Exhibit No. 106
Penthouse	Exhibit No. 104	Swingfire	Exhibit No. 105

The Carl-Gustav role provides a mounting bar across the centre of the mortar hatch to carry the Carl-Gustav gun and is shown on this Exhibit. Laden weight as for the APC.

Height: 6′ 2″ (*1·879 m.*).   Width: 9′ 3″ (*2·819 m.*).
Length: 16′ 9″ (*5·105 m.*).   Track Centres: 7′ 2″ (*2·184 m.*).
Ground Clearance: 1′ 4″ (*0·406 m.*).
Ground Pressure: 11·30 lb./sq. in. (*0·780 kg./cm.²*).
Weight: Unladen 30,300 lb. (*13,740 kg.*).   Laden 33,700 lb. (*15,286 kg.*).

Mortar Role

Description: This role mounts an 81 mm. mortar with 360° traverse. 160 rounds of ammunition are carried in suitable racks and has a crew of four. Laden weight approximately 36,000 lb.

Command Post and Penthouse Role

Description: The Command Post role provides a mapboard frame on either side having three sliding panels each with mapboards attached and tables facing either way with a centre seat. Suitable fluorescent lighting is provided above the mapboards, four lights either side. There are approximately forty varying radio installations in this role. Crew number 7. Approximate laden weight 34,000 lb.

The Penthouse role provides a 12′ long × 9′ wide × 6′ 3″ high covered area which is attached to the rear of the APC vehicle mainly in the command role. It has four fluorescent lighting units similar to those in the Command Post role which can be attached to the penthouse poles in various positions to suit the occasion. Power for the lights can either be from the vehicle system or by means of a separate battery.

Swingfire Launcher

Description: A wire-guided missile launcher on a standard F.V. 432, which can be loaded and operated by two men from under armour which is proof against shell burst and small arms. A forced ventilation system provides air pressurisation, and a heater or refrigeration unit can be connected to suit climatic conditions. The missile can be launched from either of the two tubes whenever a target is sighted in the frontal arc scanned by the periscopic sight; it is then automatically programmed on to the target sight line, when the controller applies corrections to ensure it hits the target. A 7·62 mm. MG is mounted on the 360° rotating cupola. The vehicle is air-portable and can swim from ship to shore with the built-in flotation screen erected. Power is from a K60 multi-fuel engine through an automatic gearbox and controlled differential steering.

Length: 16′ 9″ (*5·105 m.*).   Width: 9′ 9″ (*2·972 m.*).

Height: 8′ 10½″ (*2·705 m.*).   Ground clearance: 1′ 4″ (*0·406 m.*).

Weight: Unladen 32,000 lb. (*12,515 kg.*). Laden 35,500 lb. (*16,200 kg.*).

   16·1 Tonnes

Winch and Earth Anchor Role

Description: As mentioned in Exhibit No. 102 the F.V. 432 can be fitted with a Winch, Winch sub-frame and Earth Anchor so that the vehicle is capable of recovering other members of the F.V. 430 family. The winch is mechanically driven from the power take-off on the engine transfer case.

Max. line pull: 8 tons (*8,133 kg.*).

Max. pull: 16 tons (*16,266 kg.*) (using 2 part tackle).

Max. line speed at max. load: 25 ft./min. (*7·64 m./min.*).

Carrier, Maintenance, Full Tracked

Description: This vehicle is a member of the F.V.430 family of light tracked vehicles. It has been designed to carry major assemblies, or replacement power packs for AFV casualties, and will be used by REME Units for field repairs. Stowed on the vehicles are special tools and equipment to facilitate replacement of the damaged assemblies. The lifting device is a Hiab crane specially adapted for this vehicle. A crew of four is carried, made up of the driver, the commander, and two fitters. In action the commander supervises the repair operation, the vehicle driver operates the crane, and the two fitters work on the casualty. The flotation equipment consists of a collapsible screen permanently fitted to the top of the vehicle, and a buoyancy trimmer fitted for the front of the hull. Ventilation and heating equipment is provided for crew comfort in adverse conditions.

The lifting capacity of the crane ranges from—
2,750 lb. (*1,248 kg.*) at 13′ 0″ (*3·96 m.*) radius to 6,720 lb. (*3,045 kg.*) at 7′ 5″ (*2·26 m.*) radius.

Height: Travelling 9′ 3½″ (*2·83 m.*).   Length: 18′ 9½″ (*5·72 m.*).
Width: 9′ 4″ (*2·84 m.*).   Track centres: 7′ 2″ (*2·18 m.*).
Weight: Unladen 33,166 lb. (*15,044 kg.*). Laden: 39,124 lb. (*17,746 kg.*).

S.P. Mortar Locating Radar

Description: This vehicle forms yet another member of the F.V. 430 Series. The front of the vehicle and the automotive components are identical to those of the F.V. 432 A.P.C. but the rear of the hull is cut away to provide a mounting for the 'Green Archer' Mortar Locating Radar equipment. This unit is capable of accurately locating enemy mortar positions and passing the information on to the artillery for subsequent destruction of the mortar positions.

The Mk. 2 radar equipment is shown mounted on the vehicle exhibit but this may be replaced by the Mk. 4 equipment in production.

The crew comprises three men: the driver, Commander and radio operator. Heating and ventilation equipment is provided to improve the working conditions for the crew in both hot and cold climatic conditions. To facilitate the crossing of water obstacles, a built-in flotation screen is fitted to the roof of the hull. Miscellaneous items of stowage are carried on the hull or in a special locker at the rear of the vehicle.

Wombat Role

Description: This role consists of an infantry recoiless anti-tank gun mounting giving facilities to fire the Wombat from the vehicle, also the ability to stow the Wombat in the vehicle so that it can be removed for firing from the ground. Fourteen rounds of ammunition are carried in this role. The vehicle has a crew of four. Approximate laden weight 35,000 lb.

F.V. 4003

Tank A.V.R.E. Centurion Mk. 5

Description: A medium Tank developed for use by Royal Engineers, with a crew of five and carrying a 165 mm. Demolition Charge Projector. It also embodies hydraulically operated bulldozing equipment. The equipment includes a fascine and a rotatable towing hook capable of electrically jettisoning a trailer.

Height: 9' 10½" (*2·5 m.*).
Width: Basic 11' 1½" (*3·39 m.*).   Over dozer blade 13' 0" (*3·95 m.*).
Length: Over blades and hook 28' 6" (*8·7 m.*).
Weight: Unladen 109,140 lb. (*49,500 kg.*) with blade and fascine cradle.
Laden 114,219 lb. (*51,800 kg.*).

Tank Bridgelayer Centurion Mk. 5

Description: The Centurion Bridgelayer is used for launching a Class 80 single-span bridge across rivers or gaps up to 45′ wide. It is fully armoured and is normally used in the assault phase of a crossing, the bridge being laid in less than 2 minutes. By the addition of a hand-laid centre deck between the trackways, the bridge will carry the complete range of 'A' and 'B' vehicles.

Dimensions with Bridge on the Vehicle:

Height: 12′ 9″ (*3·88 m.*).   Length: 53′ 6″ (*16·3 m.*).

Width: 14′ 0″ (*4·26 m.*).

Weight: Laden 111,300 lb. (*50,400 kg.*). Unladen 107,500 lb. (*48,700 kg.*).

Tank ARK Centurion Mk. 5

Description: This vehicle is used for spanning gaps of up to 75′ wide, the vehicle itself entering the obstacle and acting as a central pier. The trackways can be launched prior to entering the gap or in the gap depending on the nature and slopes of the banks. The launching is carried out hydraulically by means of a pump driven from the main engine.

Dimensions with trackways in travelling position:

Length: 34′ 0″ (*10·37 m.*).   Width: 13′ 0″ (*3·96 m.*).
Height: 12′ 9″ (*3·88 m.*).
Weight: Laden 114,000 lb. approx. (*51,800 kg.*).

Centurion w/Rigid Panel Flotation Equipment

Description: The above illustration depicts a prototype version of the Centurion rigid panel flotation equipment. This flotation equipment comprises a sealed decking at track guard level on to which is erected, by the vehicle crew, twelve lightweight panels—four at each side, two at front and two at rear. These panels are supported and restrained in position by spring-loaded side bolsters and straining ropes. The bolsters and strainers are all connected to a single blow-out pin located on the top of the turret. Sealing of the panels is effected by a proofed fabric cover which is rolled up corset-wise around the erected panels. Jettisoning of the equipment is achieved by blowing the cover off with Cordex and detonating the blow-out pin. The production version however dispenses with the fabric cover and sealing is effected by sealing strips built into the panels.

Dimensions of vehicle with panels erected:
Length: Overall 32′ 3″ (*9·83 m.*) gun to rear.   Width: 11′ 9″ (*3·58 m.*).
Height: 12′ 0″ (*3·66 m.*).
Weight of panels (12): 1,500 lb. approx. (*680 kg.*).

PART 2

This section of the
catalogue shows exhibits
for military use sponsored
and produced by
BRITISH INDUSTRY but
not in co-operation with
F.V.R.D.E.

Tractor 30 Ton for Semi-Trailer 6 x 6 Scammell Constructor
(with Crane 50 Ton Semi-Trailer Tank Transporter)

Description: This vehicle is the motive unit for the 'Crane' 50/60 ton semi-trailer. It has six wheel drive and possesses a good cross country-performance. The cab accommodates two passengers in addition to the driver. A 15 ton (*15·3 tonne*) winch with 450 feet (*137 m.*) of rope is fitted for loading the semi-trailer and for self recovery.

Height: 10′ 11″ (*3·33 m.*).   Length: 24′ 5¼″ (*7·45 m.*).
Width: 10′ 1¼″ (*3·08 m.*).   Wheelbase: 15′ 10½″ (*4·84 m.*).
Track: Front 7′ 4″ (*2·24 m.*).   Rear 7′ 3 5⁄16″ (*2·22 m.*).
Weight: Unladen 29,500 lb. (*13,381 kg.*).

PERFORMANCE DATA
Speed, average maximum: Road 35 m.p.h. (*56·3 km./h.*).
Gross power weight ratio (b.h.p. per ton): 2·25.
Maximum tractive effort, low gear (lb. per ton): 555.

TECHNICAL DATA

Power Unit
Type: Rolls-Royce type C6 NFL.
Displacement: 12,170 c.c.
(743 ins³).
Gross B.H.P.: 200 at 2,100 r.p.m.
Gross torque: lb. ft. 550 at 1,300 r.p.m.
Governed speed: 2,100 r.p.m.
Ignition type: Compression.
Fuel System
Fuel capacity: 140 gallons (*637 litres*).
Engine Lubrication
System: Wet sump forced feed.
Engine Cooling
System: Pressurised.
Wheels
Rims: 4 piece disc type.
Tyres: 14·00″ × 20″ C.C.

Tyre pump: Inflator hose from pressure brake system.
Transmission
Clutch: Single plate.
Gearbox: ⎱
Transfer box: ⎰ 12 speed.
Propeller shafts: Hardy Spicer.
Axles: Fully floating.
Ratios: top 8·44:1, bottom 170·3:1.
Differentials: Two.
Brakes
Foot: Two line air pressure system.
Hand: Mechanical rear only.
Steering
System: Cam and double roller.
Suspension
Front: Coil springs.
Rear: Semi-elliptic.

Crane 50 Ton Semi-Trailer Tank Transporter

Description: This semi-trailer together with Tractor 30 ton for semi-trailer 6 × 6 Scammell Constructor forms a tank transportation train for the road movement of A.F.Vs. or miscellaneous stores up to 50 tons weight.
Height: 8′ 7″ (*2·62 m.*).   Length: 38′ 7½″ (*11·77 m.*).
Width: 11′ 0″ (*3·35 m.*).   Wheelbase (to king pin) 28′ 5″ (*8·66 m.*).
Track: Inner 3′ 0″ (*0·91 m.*).   Outer 9′ 0″ (*2·74 m.*).
Weight: Unladen 35,728 lb. (*16,206 kg.*). Laden 170,240 lb. (*77·219 kg.*)
Platform height: 3′ 9⅞″.

TECHNICAL DATA

Wheels
Rims: 37·5″ × 20″.
Tyres: E.20 Michelin Metallic.
Brakes
Service: 2 line air pressure/hydraulic system.
Parking: Mechanical/hydraulic hand operated.

Jacking
Manually operated hydraulic jacks.
Suspension
Unsprung walking bean.
Towing Attachments
King pin size: 3½″ dia. (*0·089 m.*).

MANUFACTURERS

Chassis: ⎱
Body: ⎰ SCAMMELL LORRIES LTD., Watford, Herts.
Transporter: CRANES (DEREHAM) LTD., Dereham, Norfolk.

Tank Medium Centurion
(fitted with the Swingfire anti tank guided weapon system)

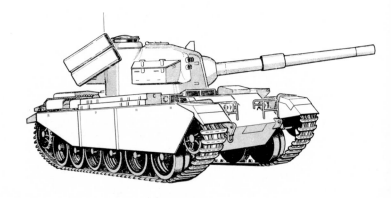

Description: A medium tank carrying a crew of four. In addition to its 105 mm. H.V. gun and stowage for 70 rounds of ammunition the vehicle on exhibition has two ready to fire Swingfire missiles mounted on either side of the turret, spare missiles are mounted on the aft face of the turret.

Periscopes are provided for terrain scanning and missile guidance. The gun control equipment ensures automatic stabilisation through a velocity sensitive control when the vehicle exceeds four m.p.h.

The vehicle characteristics are similar to the standard model.

MANUFACTURER

Guided Weapon System: BRITISH AIRCRAFT CORPORATION.

EXHIBIT **C**

Vickers Tank

Description: The Vickers Tank is designed to meet the needs of those countries which desire a tank in the 35-40 ton class.

It combines the excellent firepower provided by the 105 mm. H.V. gun with stabilised fire control system, including the ranging machine gun, with many of the automotive components of Chieftain.

The armour protection is the best possible within an overall weight of 37½ tons.

The Swingfire guided weapon system may be fitted to provide a long range anti-tank capability.

The whole provides a hard hitting, fast and agile modern fighting vehicle.

The Vickers Tank is currently in production at Vickers for the Indian Army, it is also being manufactured by the Indian Government in a new factory in Madras.

Height: 8′ 4″ (*2·538 m.*).   Length: 23′ 11″ (*7·29 m.*).
Width 10′ 4¾″ (*3·168 m.*).
Weight: Laden 37½ tons (*38·1 metric tons*).   Unladen 35½ tons (*36·0 metric tons*).

Armoured Car 6 x 6 (Saladin) Mk. 2
(fitted with the Swingfire anti tank guided
weapon system)

Description: This vehicle carries a crew of three and is used with infantry and armoured formations in the reconnaissance and pursuit role. The armament consists of a 76 mm. quick firing gun, two 0·30″ machine guns and a Swingfire missile mounted on each side of the turret. Stowage is provided in the hull for 43 rounds of ammunition and two spare missiles are carried in lieu of external bins. Periscopes are provided for closed down scanning and missile guidance. The commander can control the missiles from within the vehicle or from a separated position by using a combined sight/controller and a separation cable.

The vehicle performance and technical data is similar to the standard Saladin, F.V. 601(C) Exhibit No. 87.

MANUFACTURER

Vehicle: ALVIS LTD.
Guided Weapon System: BRITISH AIRCRAFT CORPORATION.

Armoured Carrier 6 x 6 Personnel (Saracen) (fitted with the Swingfire anti tank guided weapon system)

Description: This vehicle is an adaptation of the Saracen armoured personnel carrier Mk. 2 F.V. 603(B) to enable it to be used in the anti tank support role. The vehicle has a crew of three, armament consists of two Swingfire missiles mounted either side of the hull and a turret mounted 0·30″ machine gun. Stowage is provided within the vehicle for six spare missiles. A one metre retractable sight is fitted aft of the turret for missile guidance and terrain scanning. The periscope allows the missiles to be fired with only the periscope showing above cover. The Commander can control the missiles from within the vehicle or from a remote position by using a combined sight/controller and a separation cable.

The vehicle performance and technical data is similar to the standard Saracen, Exhibit No. 86.

MANUFACTURER

Vehicle: ALVIS LTD.
Guided Weapon System: BRITISH AIRCRAFT CORPORATION.

Armoured Patrol Car

Description: This vehicle carries a crew of three, and is designed to fulfil economically a wide variety of roles such as border patrol, convoy escort, reconnaissance and internal security duties.

The hull and turret are of welded armour plate. Armament consists of a 0·30″ Browning Machine Gun, with turret mounted smoke projectors if desired.

Height: 7′ 6″ (*2·29 m.*).   Length: 15′ 1″ (*4·60 m.*).
Width: 15′ 10″ (*1·78 m.*).   Wheelbase: 9′ 1″ (*2·77 m.*).
Track: Front 4′ 5½″ (*1·36 m.*).   Rear 4′ 5½″ (*1·36 m.*).
Weight: Unladen 6,200 lb. (*2,812 kg.*).   Laden 6,950 lb. (*3,132 kg.*).

PERFORMANCE DATA

Speed, average maximum:
    Road 50 m.p.h. (*80·47 km./h.*).
    C.C. 30 m.p.h. (*48·28 km./h.*). dependent on terrain.
Range of action at average maximum speed: 200 miles (*322 km.*).
400 miles (*644 km.*). With long range tanks.

Gross power weight ratio (b.h.p. per ton): 24·48
Maximum tractive effort, low gear (lb. per ton): 1,240.
Maximum climbing ability: 1 in 2.
Maximum gradient for stop and restart: 1 in 2.

TECHNICAL DATA

Power Unit
Type: Rover 4-cyl. petrol.
Displacement: 2,286 c.c.
Gross B.H.P.: 77 at 4,100 r.p.m.
Nett torque: 116 lb. ft. at 1,500 r.p.m.
Governed speed: Max. speed 4,100 r.p.m.
Ignition (type): Coil, 12 volt negative earth.

Fuel System
Type: Pressurised.
Type of fuel: Petrol.
Air cleaner: Oil bath type.
Fuel capacity: 14 gallons (standard) (28 gallons with long range tanks fitted).

Engine Lubrication
System: Full pressure.

Engine Cooling
System: Water cooled pressurised with pump, fan and thermostat.

Wheels
Rims: 6·50″ L × 16″.
Tyres: 9.00″ × 16″.
Tyre pump: Hand pump.
Chains: None.

Transmission
Clutch: Hydraulic single dry plate 9″ dia.
Gearbox: Single helical constant mesh, synchro-mesh top and third.
Transfer box: 2-speed reduction on main gearbox output.

Transmission—*continued*
Transfer box ratios: High 1·148 : 1, low: 2·4 : 1.
Propeller shafts: Open type to both axles.
Axles: E.N.V. automotive type.
Ratios: 4·7 to 1 front and rear.
Differentials: Spiral bevel.
Differential locks: None.

Brakes
Foot: Hydraulic power assisted.
Hand: Transmission mechanical.
Trailer: none.
Warning device: None.

Steering
System: Recirculating ball.
Turning circle: R.H. 58′ 3″ (*17·75 m.*), L.H. 58′ 3″ (*17·75 m.*).

Suspension
Front: Heavy duty semi-elliptical leaf springs.
Rear: Heavy duty semi-elliptical leaf springs with Aeon Spring assistors.
Shock absorbers: Telescopic shock absorbers.

Towing Attachments
Type: Twin hooks, front and rear.

Electrical Equipment
Generator: Dynamo Lucas C40/1 standard. Alternator extra.
Batteries: One 12 volt heavy duty.
Suppression: Limited for VHF standard. Full suppression extra.

MANUFACTURERS

Chassis: ROVER CO. LTD.
Body: SHORT BROTHERS AND HARLAND LTD. Mechanical Handling Division.

Index to Vehicles

Vehicle			Exhibit No.	F.V. Serial No.
Truck	¾ ton	Cargo (Rover ¾ ton for Powered Trailers)	21	—
Truck	1 ton	Cargo Forward Control (Rover 1 ton 4×4)	22	—
Truck	1½ ton	Cargo (Austin 1½ ton 4×4)	23	—
Truck	1½ ton	Cargo (Rover 1½ ton 4×4)	24	—
Truck	1½ ton	Cargo (Bedford 1½ ton 4×4)	25	—
Truck	1½ ton	Cargo (Commer 1½ ton 4×4)	26	—
Truck	3 ton	Tipper (Bedford 3 ton S.W.B. 4×4)	27	13111
Truck	3 ton	Dental Clinic Truck Mounted (Bedford 3 ton 4×4)	28	13165
Truck	3 ton	Automotive Repair Shop Truck Mounted (Bedford 3 ton 4×4)	29	13113
Truck	3 ton	Cargo—Air Portable Dropside (Bedford 3 ton 4×4)	30	13142(A)
Truck	3 ton	Cargo—Dropside (Bedford 3 ton 4×4)	31	13112
Truck	4½ ton	Cargo (Bedford RK 4½ ton 4×4)	32	13801
Truck	4½ ton	Cargo (Bedford RK 4½ ton 4×4 with Aluminium Body)	33	13801
Truck	4½ ton	Cargo with Winch (Bedford RK 4½ ton 4×4 with Steel Body)	34	13803
Truck	4½ ton	Cargo with Winch (Bedford RK 4½ ton 4×4)	35	13803
Truck	4½ ton	Cargo (Austin FJ 4½ ton 4×4)	36	13701
Truck	4½ ton	Cargo with Winch (Austin FJ 4½ ton 4×4)	37	13703
Truck	4½ ton	Cargo (Commer CB 4½ ton 4×4)	38	13901
Truck	4½ ton	Cargo with Winch (Commer CB 4½ ton 4×4)	39	13903
Truck	5 ton	Cargo H.M.L.C. (Alvis Stalwart Mk. 2 6×6)	90	622
Truck	10 ton	Cargo Dropside (Leyland 10 ton 6×6)	92	1121
Truck	10 ton	Cargo with Winch (A.E.C. 10 ton Mk. 3 6×6)	93	11047
	10 ton	Chassis Wheeled Self Propelled (A.E.C. 10 ton Mk. 3 6×6)	94	11046
	10 ton	Chassis Wheeled Self Propelled (Leyland 10 ton 6×6 S.W.B.)	95	—
Truck	10 ton	Missile Transporter (A.E.C. 10 ton 4×2)	96	11081

		Vehicle	*Exhibit No.*	*F.V. Serial No.*
Truck	**10 ton**	Chassis A.E.C. 10 ton 6×6 with Special Tipping Platform Body RE (BRI-MEC)	**97**	
Tractor	**10 ton**	Wheeled General Service for 8 in. Howitzer (Leyland 10 ton 6×6)	**91**	1122
Tractor	**10 ton**	Wheeled General Service Medium Artillery (Leyland 10 ton 6×6)	**98**	1103
Tractor	**20 ton**	Wheeled Semi Trailer (Scammell 20 ton 6×6)	**55**	12102
Tractor	**20 ton**	Wheeled General Service (Scammell 20 ton 6×6)	**56**	12105
Tractor	**30 ton**	Wheeled Semi Trailer (Thornycroft Antar Mk. 3 30 ton 6×4)	**53**	12004
Tractor	**30 ton**	Wheeled General Service with Ballast Body (Thornycroft Antar Mk. 3 30 ton 6×4)	**54**	12004

RECOVERY VEHICLES

			Exhibit No.	*F.V. Serial No.*
	3 ton	Recovery Vehicle Wheeled—Light (Bedford 3 ton 4×4)	**40**	13115
	10 ton	Recovery Vehicle Wheeled—Medium (A.E.C. Mk. 2 10 ton 6×6)	**41**	11044
	10 ton	Recovery Vehicle Wheeled—Heavy (Leyland 10 ton 6×6)	**42**	1119
Trailer	**10 ton**	Recovery (10 ton)	**42A**	3221
Trailer	**10/30 ton**	Dummy Axle Recovery (10/30 ton)	**43**	3561

CONTAINER BODIES

			Exhibit No.	*F.V. Serial No.*
	1 ton	Container Transportable Vehicle Mounted (1 ton)	**44**	CB.101
	1 ton	Container Transportable (1 ton)	**47**	CB.101
	3 ton	Container Transportable Vehicle Mounted (3 ton)	**45**	CB.302
	3 ton	Container Transportable (3 ton)	**46**	CB.305
	3 ton	Container Transportable, Electronic Repair SAGW No. 2, Vehicle Mounted (3 ton)	**50**	CB.352
	3 ton	Container Transportable, Radar Repair F.A. No. 8 Mk. 1, Vehicle Mounted (3 ton)	**51**	CB.354

233

	Vehicle		*Exhibit No.*	*F.V. Serial No.*
		Container Equipment Transportable (6 ft. × 6 ft. × 6 ft.)	**48**	—
		Container Body (Aircon B)	**52**	—
Trailer	**5 ton**	Transporter Container Body	**49**	2829(D)

MISCELLANEOUS VEHICLES

	¾ ton	Ambulance 2/4 Stretcher (Rover 9 ¾ ton 4×4)	**17**	18067
Truck	**¾ ton**	Fire Fighting—Airfield Crash Rescue (Rover ¾ ton 4×4)	**58**	18047
Truck	**3 ton**	Tanker, Fuel, Servicing Aircraft (1,000 gallon Air Portable Bedford 3 ton 4×2)	**62**	13199
		Motor Coach Large with Ambulance Role (Bedford 4×2 39 seat/ 16 Stretcher)	**64**	13198(A)
Truck	**5 ton**	Fire Fighting Foam (Alvis Mk. 6A 6×6)	**59**	652
Truck	**5 ton**	Fire Fighting Foam (Thornycroft Nubian Mk. VII 6×6)	**60**	—
Truck	**5 ton**	Tanker, Fuel, Servicing Aircraft (2,000 gallon Air Portable A.E.C. Mercury 4×2)	**63**	12381
Truck	**10 ton**	Fire Fighting Foam (Thornycroft Nubian Major 6×6)	**61**	—
		Armoured Command Vehicle— Heavy (A.E.C. 10 ton 6×6)	**89**	11061
		Trenching Machine Wheeled (Thornycroft)	**57**	—

SEMI TRAILERS

	50 ton	Semi Trailer Tank Transporter (50 ton)	**53A**	3011

TRAILERS

Trailer	**50 ton**	Tank Transporter No. 1 Mk. 3 (50 ton)	**54A**	3601
Trailer	**7½ ton**	Equipment Radar, Trailer Mounted A.A. No. 10 Mk. 1 (7½ ton)	**68**	2824

234

Vehicle			Exhibit No.	F.V. Serial No.
Trailer	**5 ton**	Equipment Radar, Trailer Mounted SAGW A.A. No. 12 Mk. 1 (5 ton)	**65**	2828
Trailer	**5 ton**	Antenna SAGW A.A. No. 11 (5 ton)	**66**	2826
Trailer	**5 ton**	Equipment Radar Trailer Mounted SAGW A.A. No. 11 Mk. 1 (5 ton)	**67**	2827
Trailer	**2 ton**	Photographic Film Processing Hand Trailer Mounted (2 ton Air Portable)	**69**	2504(C)
Trailer	**2 ton**	Low Platform, Earth Moving Ancillaries (2 ton)	**70**	2508
Trailer	**2 ton**	Flat Platform (2 ton)	**71**	2505(D)
Trailer	**1 ton**	Class 16 Air Portable Bridge (1 ton)	**72**	2420
Trailer	**1 ton**	Supply SAGW.ET316 (1 ton)	**73**	2411
Trailer	**1 ton**	Generating Set, Diesel Engine, 10 KVA Trailer Mounted (1 ton)	**74**	2401(R)
Trailer	**1 ton**	Cargo (1 ton)	**75**	2401(A)
Trailer	**1 ton**	Air Conditioner, Trailer Mounted (No. 54, Mk. 2, 1 ton)	**76**	2401(T)
Trailer	**1 ton**	Cargo Power Driven (1 ton)	**21A**	—
Trailer	**¾ ton**	Water Purification Unit, Trailer Mounted (1,000 g.p.h. ¾ ton)	**77**	2308(A)(4)
Trailer	**¾ ton**	Welding Set Lightweight, Trailer Mounted (¾ ton)	**78**	2365
Trailer	**¾ ton**	Cargo (¾ ton)	**6**	2361
Trailer	**¾ ton**	Tanker Water (100 gallon ¾ ton)	**8**	2362

ARMOURED FIGHTING VEHICLES (WHEELED)

Vehicle	Exhibit No.	F.V. Serial No.
Carrier Personnel Wheeled A.P.C. Mk. 2 (Alvis Saracen 6×6)	**86**	603(B)
Armoured Car 76 mm. gun (Alvis Saladin Mk. 2 6×6)	**87**	601(C)
Armoured Car Floating (Alvis Saladin 6×6)	**88**	601(C)
Scout Car Liaison Mk. 1/1 (Daimler Ferret 4×4)	**79**	701(J)
Scout Car Floating Mk. 1/1 (Daimler Ferret 4×4)	**80**	701(J)
Scout Car L.V.R. Mk. 1/2 (Daimler Ferret 4×4)	**81**	704
Scout Car Reconnaissance Mk. 2/3 (Daimler Ferret 4×4)	**82**	701(H)
Scout Car Reconnaissance/GW Mk. 2/6 (Daimler Ferret 4×4)	**83**	703
Scout Car Reconnaissance Mk. 4 (Daimler Ferret 4×4 Big Wheeled)	**84**	711

Vehicle	Exhibit No.	F.V Serial No.
Scout Car Reconnaissance/GW Mk. 5 (Daimler Ferret 4×4 Big Wheeled)	**85**	712

ARMOURED FIGHTING VEHICLES (TRACKED)

Chieftain Mk. 2	**99**	4201
Abbot	**100**	433
432 Series in the following roles:		
Ambulance	**101**	432
Armoured Personnel Carrier	**102**	432
Mortar	**103**	432
Command and Penthouse	**104**	432
Swingfire Role	**105**	432
Winch and Earth Anchor	**106**	432
Carrier, Maintenance, Full Tracked	**107**	434
SP. Mortar Locating Radar	**108**	436
Wombat and Miser Role	**109**	432

Index to Manufacturers of Vehicles

**The above index identifies the manufacturers associated with the
production of the exhibit.**

NOTES

NOTES

NOTES